Open Door to Plants

John Bartram Speaks

One day I was busy in holding my plough (for thou seest I am but a simple ploughman), and, being aweary I sat me beneath the shade of a tree to rest myself. I cast my eyes upon a daisy. I plucked the pretty flower, and, viewing it with more closeness than common farmers are wont to bestow upon a weed, I observed therein many curious and distinct parts, each perfect in itself, and each in its way tending to enhance the beauty of the flower. What a shame, said my mind, — or something within my mind, — what a shame that thou has spent so many years in the ruthless destroying of that which the Lord in his infinite goodness hath made so perfect in its humble place, without thy trying to understand one of its simplest leaves. This thought awakened my curiosity, for these are not the thoughts to which I had been accustomed. I returned to my plough once more, but this new desire for inquiry into the perfections the Lord hath granted to all about us did not quit my mind; nor hath it since.

JOHN BARTRAM (1699-1777)

OPEN DOOR TO PLANTS

by
Dr. J. H. Standen

Drawings by Mary Standen Turak

WILLIAM B. EERDMANS PUBLISHING COMPANY
GRAND RAPIDS, MICHIGAN

Printed in the United States of America

Dedication

To my wife,

Marguerite Laramie Standen, whose faith in her nonconforming husband has never wavered more than could reasonably be expected,

to my daughter,

Mary Standen Turak, who did the drawings very capably with one hand while managing a job, advanced studies, two babies, a home, and a husband with the other, and

to Miss Carol Woodward,

who had confidence in what started out as a very raw manuscript,

this book is most gratefully dedicated.

Foreword

From my earliest years I wanted to learn about plants, their names, their stories, their uses. I wandered much alone in the woods, and I was an enthusiastic gardener. I since found that there are many others with similar interests. I also discovered that the answers to my many questions were not always easy to find. For this reason I have written a book such as I would have enjoyed while I was groping my way toward an understanding of plants.

Plants are fundamental to life on earth, as explained in the first chapter. But plants are of importance to man in ways other than supplying him with food and clothing. Man does not live by bread alone. Much of the beauty of the world we owe to plants. Many painters have found inspiration in them. The Italian composer, Caldara, sang of the "friendly forest." Wordsworth saw "a host of golden daffodils" in the crisp spring sunlight, and expressed his approval. Most of us feel the same way about plants. Those who do not are to be pitied. The colonial versifier, Joel Barlow, had the candor to admit that "all my bones are made of Indian corn."

When a family establishes a home, plants are usually an important part of the planning — a lawn, some trees and shrubbery, a flower garden, and often a kitchen garden, are felt to be necessities. For many of us in the more northern areas, the home in winter is not complete without a few attractive house plants.

For those who wish to choose a hobby or career in the world of plants, several chapters give an introduction to the many and varied fields in botany and related areas. The concluding chapter is devoted entirely to careers and hobbies.

I have not attempted to be exhaustive in my treatment of the many botanical areas. Some of the earlier chapters are rather elementary, and the more experienced reader may want to skip over them. This book is meant to be read for pleasure as well as information. Read where your interest takes you in this miscellany, which is designed to help the reader find his way, interestingly, into the wonderful world of plants.

Contents

Thanks

Many people have been very generous of their time and knowledge during the preparation of this book. I wish most sincerely to express my gratitude to all of them, and most especially to the following:

N. J. Pierce, Chief, Special Service,[1] Veterans Administration Hospital, Northport, Long Island; Dr. George S. Avery, Jr., Director, Brooklyn Botanic Garden, Brooklyn 15, New York; Dr. Paul C. Mangelsdorf, Botanic Museum of Harvard University, Cambridge 38, Massachusetts; Dr. Charles B. Beck, Dept. of Botany, University of Michigan, Ann Arbor, Michigan; Dr. Warren H. Wagner, Jr., Dept. of Botany, University of Michigan; Dr. George Gillett, Dept. of Botany, University of Hawaii, Honolulu, Hawaii; Dr. George J. Schumacher, Division of Science and Mathematics, Harper College, State University of New York, Endidcott, New York; Dr. R. A. Deno, College of Pharmacy, University of Michigan, Ann Arbor, Michigan; Dr. G. F. Sprague, Agricultural Research Service, Field Crops Research Branch, U. S. Department of Agriculture, Beltsville, Maryland; Dr. Jean L. Laffon, Dept. of Zoology and Entomology, Iowa State University, Ames, Iowa; Dr. E. P. Sylwester, Dept. of Botany and Plant Pathology, Iowa State University, Ames, Iowa; Dr. Wilson N. Stewart, Dept. of Botany, University of Illinois, Urbana, Illinois; Dr. William S. Benninghoff, Dept. of Botany, University of Michigan, Ann Arbor, Michigan; Dr. K. L. Jones, Chairman, Dept. of Botany, University of Michigan, Ann Arbor, Michigan; Dr. A. G. Norman, Botanical Gardens, University of Michigan, Ann Arbor, Michigan; Dr. Joseph C. Gilman, Dept. of Botany and Plant Pathology, Iowa State Univesity, Ames, Iowa; Robert J. Eiserle, Fritzsche Brothers, Inc., New York 11, New York; and Stephen C. Bocskey (deceased), Ferris Institute, Big Rapids, Michigan.

---

[1]Position cited in each case is that occupied by the individual at the time his services were extended to me.

CHAPTER 1

Green Plants in Relation to Life and Man

HE wonderful process called photosynthesis, which means "putting together by means of light," enables green plants to sustain themselves.

Chlorophyll, a green chemical in plants, has the ability, in the presence of sunlight, to split water (H_2O) into hydrogen (H) and oxygen (O). Much of the oxygen released in this process is returned to the air, and the remainder is used by plants in other vital processes. The released hydrogen is combined by the plant with carbon dioxide (CO_2) to form the simple sugar, glucose.

Glucose is used by plants to make more complex sugars, starches, cellulose (paper, cotton, and linen are largely cellulose) fats, and other compounds. With the addition of the elements nitrogen, phosphorus, and sulphur (N, P, S), plants, and other organisms, create proteins. Protoplasm, the living jelly of all plants and animals, is made up of protein complexes.

Not only are the simple sugars used to build more complex compounds, but the sugars, starches, fats, proteins, etc., can, through oxidative processes, furnish the energy required by all living organisms. Thus, animals eating plants, or eating animals who eat plants, have a source of compounds for building their own tissues, and for securing vital energy through the process commonly called respiration. In birds and mammals the energy thus obtained enables the creature to maintain a fairly constant body temperature, and thus to remain active, even at low temperatures.

Although plants absorb carbon dioxide from the air, the respirative processes in all organisms tend to return carbon dioxide to the air about as fast as it is removed, and the concentration is rather constant at three parts in 10,000.

Sugars, starches, fats, and proteins made by plants enable them to store food for their own use against time of need. These are often

11

concentrated in seeds, roots, bulbs, stems, tubers, or even leaves. Man, and other organisms, appropriate them for their own nutrition. (Animals also store foods against time of need. In man and many other creatures an animal starch called glycogen is stored in the liver. The fatty tissue underlying the skin serves not only as an energy reserve, but, in many animals, notably the whale, as an insulating layer to retain body heat.)

It is obvious that all life on our planet depends on photosynthesis as the ultimate source of all food and many of our sources of energy.

CHAPTER 2

Plants and Man

GREEN plants are the ultimate source of all of our food. But the relation of plants to man, and of man to plants, goes far deeper than the necessity for food. Civilization itself is based on man's use of plants.

Primitive man, like other animals, was a food gatherer. Most of his waking hours were spent in hunting, fishing, grubbing roots, gathering seeds and berries, and the like. There are still peoples on this earth who are no further along the way. If man must spend practically all day looking for something to eat, he will have precious little time or energy to devote to those activities we associate with civilization.

From grubbing a root or gathering seeds to the planting of a root or a few seeds is a short step. Some of man's primitive attempts at agriculture were fortunate enough so that different peoples emerged as food growers and ceased to be merely food gatherers.

The success of these attempts would depend on favorable soil and climatic conditions, and we find such conditions wherever civilizations have developed. Success would also depend on the amenability of plants to improvement by cultivation and selective breeding. In many food crops the ability to be stored against time of need is fundamental.

All civilizations of the past, even as those of today, have been based squarely on one or more of the cereals. In the Old World these included wheat, rice, barley, rye, oats and a few others. In the New World the Mayan, Incan, Aztec and other civilizations were all dependent on maize — today commonly called corn. Before maize was developed to anything like its present productivity, there could have been no great civilizations in the New World.

Whatever plants man grows, it is the cereals that give sufficient return for toil expended to permit storing of food against lean periods, a division of labor, and leisure time for the cultivation of

13

the arts, for learning, and all that we recognize in the word "civilization." Furthermore, the agricultural society tends to stay in one
place. It is difficult to create anything very permanent among a
people who must constantly move from place to place.

What does man need other than food? Clothing, shelter, and fuel,
first of all. If we dress in cotton, our clothing is obtained from the
cotton plant; if in linen, then from the flax plant. If we dress in
wool or silk or fur or leather, we obtain our clothing from animals
instead. But these animals are all nourished, directly or indirectly,
by green plants. Even the synthetic fibers are made from raw materials derived in one way or another from plants.

All of the wood and paper that are used in the building of our
homes come from plants. Even the cement for the concrete, the
lime for the plaster, and the glass of our windows are made with
heat obtained from plant products. For fuel we burn wood or coal,
the latter derived from plants buried in swamps millions of years
ago, or we use oil from petroleum that had its origin in microscopic
marine organisms, either green plants or animals that were dependent
upon green plants. Only if we heat with electricity derived from
water power are we able to bypass plant life in our search for
warmth.

Have you any concept of the amount of paper used by the world
each year for books, magazines, newspapers, for containers of many
kinds, for construction purposes, and in a thousand other ways?
Newsprint alone reaches astronomical proportions; for example, the
newsprint required by the *New York Times* alone requires six million trees a year.

It is estimated that the world uses around sixty billion cubic feet
of wood each year; the United States using about twenty-five billion
of it, or about 190 cubic feet per capita for North America (which
is about five times the per capita consumption of any other continent). This is used for lumber (forty billion board feet annually
in the United States), fuel, pulpwood, and for hundreds of other
products. There are at least 600,000,000 new fence posts set each
year in the United States and five million poles for power and telephone lines. Ties for railroad tracks consume vast quantities of wood
and so do mine timbers. Uses we would never suspect loom large.
Over 7,500 tons of charcoal are used annually in this country to
cure shade-grown tobacco.

From the monetary standpoint forests supply well over two billion dollars in primary products alone in the United States, while
secondary products (finished materials) reach a value several times

this large. The estimate for Michigan for a single year is half a billion dollars and for the country as a whole, eleven billion dollars. Paper and allied products from wood reach a total value of over seven billion dollars annually in the United States. If we include with forest land the land used both for forestry and for pasture, there are well over 300,000,000 acres of forest land in the United States — around twenty percent of the total area of the country.

To clothe ourselves, and for other uses, we annually grow over twenty-five million acres of cotton. Texas produces about a third of this. The crop is grown on one farm in every five in our country. Cotton is today probably the most important commodity in world commerce. The crop in the United States is valued at nearly three billion dollars annually, and the products made from it — cloth and many other manufactures — at well over twelve billion dollars at the mills. The world production of cotton is officially estimated (1962) at 11,700,000 metric tons annually (of which over one-third is produced in the United States). If this much cotton were woven into thirty-six inch percale, it would make a strip long enough to reach from the earth to the moon about 240 times! "This figure," you say, "simply can't be right. He much have made a mistake." I'll admit that I was a bit shaken myself when I first went through the calculations, but here they are:

> 11,700,000 metric tons was the official world estimate for cotton production in 1962.
> A metric ton contains 2204.6 pounds.
> It will take at least four yards of yard-wide percale to weigh one pound. (I checked this; the percale I weighed was about three and a half ounces per yard.)
> The average distance from the earth to the moon is 238,860 miles.
> There are 1,728 yards in a mile.
> Thus, the number of times such a sheet of percale would extend to the moon would be

$$X = \frac{11,700,000 \times 2204.6 \times 4}{238,860 \times 1728}$$

Because we are only looking for an approximation, simplify this a bit to

$$X = \frac{11,700,000 \times 2200 \times 4}{240,000 \times 1700}$$

(None of these simplifications will increase the value of X. The contrary is true.)

Cancel some of the zeros, and we have
$$X = \frac{117 \times 220 \times 4}{24 \times 17} = 240 \text{ plus}$$

Cotton fibre is not only used for cotton cloth, but much of it is transformed by chemical processes into rayon and other products. In addition, cotton seed supplies large quantities of cooking oils. The meal left from the pressed seed is an important cattle feed as well as raw material for the manufacture of plastics.

As we would expect, production figures for food crops are also enormous. Of the cereal crops, rice, which is the "daily bread" of much of the Orient, reaches a world production estimated at nearly seven billion bushels, nearly one-third of which is grown in China. Wheat is second on the list, with a world production of over six billion bushels, almost one-fourth of which is grown in the United States. Corn or maize follows, with a world production of around 5,300,000,000 bushels, with the United States producing around forty percent of the total. Much of this in our country is fed to livestock on the farm, but increasing amounts each year are converted into cornstarch, glucose or corn syrup, dextrin, alcohol, corn oil, corn protein (much of this is converted to synthetic fibers), and many other products. The cobs find a great many uses; among other things they are an excellent source of the industrial solvent furfural. Sweet corn and popcorn are also produced in enormous quantities. The average annual pack of sweet corn in the United States amounts to nearly 800,000,000 cans. If placed end to end, these cans would extend well over twice around the earth at the equator. If this figure seems large to you, consider how many more cans of tomatoes, tomato paste and tomato sauce we use than we do cans of corn!

Potatoes are another important world crop, the annual yield totaling around nine billion bushels. While most of these are used for food, potatoes are used in many industries, for example, for the manufacture of starch, alcohol, and dozens of other products.

All in all, the cultivated crops in this country cover nearly 330,-000,000 acres. Many crops other than the grains and cotton are produced in almost unbelievable amounts. The value of our tobacco crop each year exceeds $900,000,000 and is made into products valued (at the factory) at well over $2,500,000,000. Crops of which we may be scarcely aware are often astonishingly large. For example, around $200,000,000 worth of flax seed (for paint oil and other uses) are produced each year in our country.

When we travel abroad we find crops of great importance, the very names of which are new to us. In central and northern South America cassava (obtained from the root of *Manihot esculenta*) supplies, along with corn, the daily bread of much of the populace. The annual production of cassava is estimated at fourteen million pounds. The cleaned, peeled roots are grated and the product baked, often in the form of a large thin disc. The first time my wife was served one of these, she thought it was some sort of table mat. The flavor much resembles that of a table mat, too.

On the west coast of South America, quinoa seed (*Chenopodium Quinoa*) is obtained from a relative of our common weed called lambsquarter. (Our garden beet is a bit more distantly related to it.) These seeds are made into a meal which is used in enormous quantities.

If we travel in India and many other parts of the world, we encounter the chick pea (*Cicer arientinum*). If you have been in South America, you may be familiar with these as garbanzos. The chick pea is used to some extent in the United States, particularly among peoples whose ancestors came from the Mediterranean area and the Near East. The peas, which are related to the garden pea, are commonly sold as the dried, matured seed, about a half-inch in diameter, with a couple of very characteristic indentations on the surface. I have heard it said that the Roman statesman Cicero got his name because the end of his (or an ancestor's) nose looked like a chick pea (*Cicer*). Be that as it may, the annual production of this one crop is valued at well over $100,000,000.

If we use fish or other sea food in our diet, we again are dependent on plants, because it is the microscopic plant life in rivers, lakes, and oceans that in the last analysis, supplies sustenance for whatever food we obtain from those sources. Livestock for food, milk, wool, leather, and other products require pasture or range land, and this amounts to around sixty percent of the total land area or over a billion acres in the United States. Certain grasses and legumes supply far better forage than others; there is considerable activity throughout the country to improve pastures by use of better forage crops, fertilization, and improved management to obtain greater "carrying capacity." One of these more productive forage crops — alfalfa — covers fifteen million acres in the United States. If this were in a single field, it would be over 160 miles square.

However, all of these impressive figures are to be expected. There are a great many people in this world, and all of them would like to eat three meals a day, have clothes to cover themselves, and a home to live in. This just naturally adds up to quite enormous quantities of food, fabric and lumber for shelter each year, all of which must trace back to plants.

The fact that no country is self-sufficient in plant products brings about world trade, and upon this world trade rests much of man's history. If a nation outstrips its food supply, it is apt either to decline or to invade its neighbors land, as the Italians did in Ethiopia or the Japanese in Korea and Mongolia, and more history is made.

The importance of maintaining our sources of plant products in a condition of vigorous productivity is obvious, if we consider the inevitable results if this is lost. Erosion can ruin soils, and this has occurred in many parts of the world, for example, over much of China. Recurrent famines and a low standard of living are the result. We had a bad taste of this in Oklahoma a few years ago. It is interesting that between 1917 and 1940 New York State suffered a net decline of thirty-nine paper mills and fifty-six pulp mills, almost entirely due to the exhaustion of pulpwood supplies. On the brighter side, we occasionally come across statements like this: "A few intensively managed (forest) properties are yielding two to five times the average return per acre." This, and other similar reports, indicates that man is beginning, rather slowly, to take a careful look at conservation for the future.

Our discussion so far as been concerned with products built up by plants. We should be very much aware, however, of the importance to the world of those plants that tear down, rather than build up. As soon as a plant or animal dies, bacteria and fungi, which are simple plants, begin the job of returning the materials of which the plant or animal was composed to the soil and to the atmosphere in forms that will again be used by still other generations of green plants.

Plants that cover the earth not only help to make it a beautiful place in which to live, but also help to temper the weather and aid in water retention. Man is dependent on plants in many respects. Conversely, many plants are absolutely dependent on man. A high proportion of our cultivated plants could not continue to exist without man to care for them. One example: if man were to become extinct, there would not be a single corn (maize) plant living after two or three years.

CHAPTER 3

Getting Acquainted

HERE are so many different kinds of plants in the world that no one could know all of them. However, if you are interested, you can learn a great many of them, and rather easily. You can at least place many of them in families, and once this is done their precise identification is much simpler.

We will concentrate in this discussion on plants of the United States, north of the Gulf States, and east of the Rockies. However, many of the ideas here included can be applied to plants all over the world. I have walked into tropical jungles and identified plants I had never seen before. It is not impossible if one has an understanding of the basic patterns concerned in plant relationships. If you encounter something you cannot identify, mentally file it away for the future.

Trees constitute an ideal starting point. These can be identified in summer or winter, with or without flowers, and rather easily. For the trees in the area covered here, the first separation would be between the pines[1] and the non-pines, commonly called broadleaves. The pine group has either needlelike, or scalelike foliage.

If the foliage is needlelike (or like a flattened needle), the leaves may be borne many in a cluster, five in a cluster, two in a cluster, or singly. If they are many in a cluster, dropping in the winter, leaving twigs covered with warty leaf bases, it will be a larch or tamarack. The native tamarack grows in wet places. If the needles are five in a cluster, it will be one of the white pine series. If they are two in a cluster, it will be pine, possibly red pine (called Norway pine in error), jack pine, Austrian pine, Scotch pine, etc. If the needles are borne singly, and are square in cross section (roll one between finger and thumb) it is a spruce. If they are flat, it is

---

[1]You may live far enough south so that the tree called Australian Pine is grown in your community. It is not at all related to true pine and is not covered in this book.

probably a hemlock, balsam fir, or yew. The hemlock leaves are short and do not have a very good odor. The balsam fir leaves are longer and have a very pleasant odor. The yew leaves are very dark green, and the tree is usually small. The fruit of the yew is a rose-pink gelatinous berry.

If the foliage is scalelike but soft to the touch the tree will be arbor vitae, commonly called white or swamp cedar. If harsh to the touch or briary, it will be juniper, commonly called red cedar. (There are shrubby, or even creeping, species.) The giant sequoia of eastern California has similar foliage.

Redwood, also a California tree, has leaves much like the hemlock, and so does the bald cypress. However, you are not apt to encounter redwoods east of the Rockies, and bald cypress is usuallly fairly far south. It does come up into the Mississippi basin quite a way, though. You'll always find it growing in swamps, and, like the tamarack-larch group, it drops its needles in winter.

That finishes our introduction to the pines and their relatives in the area we are covering. If you want to find exact species, any good tree guide will enable you to do so easily, unless it is an exotic form. Remember, too, that the pine family is world-wide, so be prepared to encounter new ones as you travel.

With two exceptions, broadleaf trees in our area fall into three groups, based on leaf arrangement on the twigs. One of the exceptions is the native catalpa, which has the large, heart-shaped leaves arranged around the stem at each node (bump) in groups of three. The heavy twigs, foul-smelling when broken, and the fruit, shaped like very long cigars, make this tree easily identified.

The second exception is the Asiatic ginkgo, commonly planted as an ornamental, which has many small, fernlike leaves clustered on stubs on twigs and branches. If it is a female tree in fruit, do not bite into the fruit; they are foul with butyric acid.

The three large groups are separated on the basis of leaf arrangement on the twigs. One of these groups has two leaves opposite each other on the twig, then, further along, a second pair, set at right angles to the first. In this group we find maples, box-elder, ash, buckeyes, horse chestnuts, and most of the dogwoods. Buckeyes and horse chestnuts have leaves cut in such a way that the several segments or leaflets come out from a central point at the tip of the leaf stalk. This is called a palmately compound arrangement. Ash trees have their several leaflets attached on either side of a long leaf stalk. This is termed pinnately compound. Box elder, which is one of the maples, has the same arrangement, but with few leaflets. The other maple leaves are all characteristically cut, though not to the central stalks, while dogwoods have regularly shaped leaves.

The second, much larger, group has the leaves two-ranked, that is, alternated in two rows along opposite sides of the twigs. Here belong sycamores, with their maplelike leaves, hop-hornbeam, with hoplike fruits, mulberries, basswood, black alders (in swamps), birches, the smooth-barked blue beech, beech[1], juneberry, also called service-berry or shadbush, hackberry, elms, Osage orange (not too strictly two-ranked), and redbud. The first means of separation that would occur to the beginner is leaf shape, and this is good, but there are many other characteristics for easy recognition. For example, the Osage orange is the only one of these with thorns. A good tree guide will now take you easily to species.

The last, and largest, group has leaves in a two-five spiral arrangement. If you count the leaves around the stem, you will count five on two times around, which means that there are about 144 degrees between leaves. Here belong black locust, honey locust, Kentucky coffee tree, mountain ash, sumacs, tree of heaven or ailanthus, black walnut, butternut, English walnut, hickories, pecan, prickly ash, apples, thorn apples, pears, plums, apricots, peaches, cherries, sweet gum, sour gum, tulip tree, sassafras, oaks, willows, poplars and aspens (including cottonwood), magnolia, and persimmon.

We can separate these further on types of leaves. All of them down through prickly ash have pinnately compound leaves. The Kentucky coffee tree and the honey locust leaves are bi-pinnate, that is, the main leaf stalk has secondary leaf stalks on either side, with the leaflets attached to the secondary leaf stalks.

If the tree has thorns or briars, it will be a honey locust, black locust, thorn apple, prickly ash, or some of the plums. A pair of briars either side of the leaf is found in black locust and prickly ash. If the tree has a branched thorn, it is a honey locust. Thorns on thorn apple and plum are spurlike. There are unarmed species or varieties in all of the above, however.

All oak twigs have a star-shaped pith (use a lens). But be careful of what to expect in an oak leaf. Those of several species, especially farther south, are perfectly smooth on the edge.

All members of the black walnut-butternut-English walnut group have chambered pith; you'll find this in relatives all over the

---

[1]The blue beech and the true beech are not closely related.

world. Cut the next black walnut twig you see to find out what this means.

But once again, get an illustrated tree guide to take you right down to species. Such a guide, together with the above outline, should enable you to identify practically every tree in your neighborhood in your spare time in far less than a month.

Another very rewarding approach to plant recognition is to learn the characteristics of a few large, easily recognized families. Then at least you will be able to narrow down your search on many specimens. Of the seed plants other than the pines and their relatives, twenty-one families cover about two-thirds of the seed plants listed in Fernald's revision of Gray's Manual of Botany. All of these families are world-wide in distribution, and once you have them well in hand, you have a fair introduction to plants wherever you go. The seed-bearing plants other than pines are divided into two large groups, the monocots and the dicots. This is what the stems of these groups look like under the microscope: Grasses, sedges, palms, lilies, and several other groups are monocots. Beans, oaks, mustards, etc. are dicots.

Figure 1

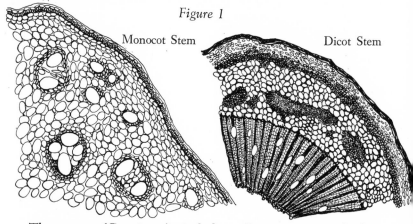

Monocot Stem   Dicot Stem

The grasses (Gramineae), including all our grains, with their relatively long, parallel-veined leaves, constitute one of the largest families, but, while it is easy to place grasses in family, separating them into species is a matter involving considerable study. It can be done — there are many guides available, and, if you go far enough into their study, you will be an agrostologist.

The enormous sedge family (Cyperaceae) closely resembles the grasses, though many of the sedges have stems that are triangular in cross section, a characteristic never found in the grasses. Practically all sedges grow in wet places — but so do a few grass species, for example, wild rice.

Most of the grasses have hollow stems, while all sedges have solid stems. Grasses with the stem filled with spongy tissue would include sorghum, sugar cane, and corn. Grasses have seeds with covering bracts that are more or less easily removed, while in the sedges, each seed has a hard covering that completely encloses it. Incidently, the first paper, papyrus, was made by the Egyptians from the sedge, *Cyperus Papyrus*.

There are a few plants with parallel-veined leaves, such as cattail, that the beginner should be wary of confusing with grasses and sedges.

While the detailed study of the enormous grass and sedge families is best left to the specialists, the members of the remaining eighteen large families covered here are rather easy for the beginner. The first thing to· do is to become familiar with the parts of the flower, so that the terms used can be understood.

Figure 2   The Parts of an Insect-Pollinated Flower

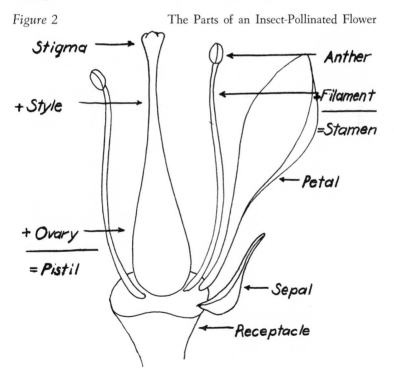

The flower serves to insure the process called pollination, without which flowering plants cannot, as a rule, produce seeds. Pollen grains must be transferred from the stamens, in which they are produced, to the parts in which the seeds will be found. The pollen transfer in different plants may be accomplished by wind, water, insects, or other means.

As you can see, the several floral parts are attached to the end of a stalk called a pedicel. In many flowers, but not all, there are green, somewhat leaflike sepals, which enclose the flower in the bud and often help support the petals once the flower opens. The function of the petals, which are usually colored other than green, is to attract the insects which will transfer the pollen. Many flowers secrete a perfume as an additional attractant, and most of them offer nectar to their visitors as well.

Each stamen is composed of a stalk, called the filament, and a head, the anther, in which the pollen grains are formed. The part in which the seeds will develop is called the pistil. It is made up of the stigma, constructed to receive the pollen grains; the style, which connects stigma and ovary (in some flowers the style is so short as to be practically non-existent); and the ovary itself. Within this the ovules, following pollination and a further sexual process called fertilization, will become seeds.

Not all flowers, however, have all of these parts. In some plant species the pollen-bearing parts are borne separately from the seed-producing parts and sometimes even on separate plants. Wind-pollinated flowers such as those of grasses and pines, have no need for attractive petals, perfume, or nectar.

In classifying plants, any one kind is called a species — and there are frequently varieties of a single species. Species that resemble each other very closely are gathered into groups called genera (singular: genus). Several genera that are considered to be closely related are placed in a plant family. (There are also broader divisions, but the beginner need not be concerned with these at first.) To illustrate, the common cabbage, together with kale, kohlrabi, cauliflower, broccoli, and brussels sprouts, are all derived from a common ancestor, the cliff cabbage, that still grows along the sea coasts of Europe. The classification for cabbage would be as follows:

Family: *Cruciferae* (The family name that means cross-bearer, is derived from the fact that the four petals of each flower in this family are borne more or less in the shape of a cross.)

Genus: *Brassica* (the mustard genus).

Species: *oleracea.*

Variety: capitata, to indicate that the plant forms a head. Each of the other varieties of *Brassica oleracea* has its own varietal name: cauliflower is variety botrytis; kohlrabi, variety caulorapa.

While these are all botanical varieties within a species of cultivated plants, we also find such varieties in species of wild plants that have not been tampered with by man. An example is the beautiful *Viola pedata* variety *bicolor,* the two-colored birdfoot violet or wild pansy that grows in southeast Iowa and elsewhere.

Continuing with the *Cruciferae,* the flowers of members of this family have, in addition to four petals, usually in the shape of a cross, four sepals, a single pistil, and six stamens. Two of the six stamens are shorter than the other four, a characteristic lacking in the closely related family, *Capparidaceae.* Members of the family contain complex sulfur compounds that give the plants a pungent, often hot, flavor.

In addition to the vegetables already mentioned, there are, in *Cruciferae,* the several radish varieties, turnip, the big, yellow-fleshed rutabaga, and others. The Chinese developed the Chinese cabbage, often called celery cabbage, and the non-heading, but similar pak-choi. Horseradish is a very "hot" member of the group, and water cress, growing at the edge of streams (very edible in salads), is another. It is *Nasturium officinale,* but do not confuse it with the garden flower called nasturium. While the latter has spicy leaves that may be used in salads, it is in the unrelated tropical family, the Tropaeolaceae.

Many garden flowers are likewise in the *Cruciferae,* including sweet allysum, candyturf, wall flower, honesty or money plant, stocks, and rocket. Most of these flowers are fragrant. The mustards are here too, and many bad weeds, discussed in a later chapter.

Another of these enormous families is the *Leguminosae,* the pea or bean family. The flowers of many, *but not all,* look something like sweet peas, with bilaterally symetrical flowers. Most of them have five sepals, five petals (of different sizes and shapes), ten stamens (one of which is shorter than the others), and a single pistil. After pollination the pistil characteristically forms a pod, more or less like a bean pod. However, there are modifications of this, as in clovers and peanuts.

Relatives grown for food include peas, beans, peanuts, pigeon peas, cow peas, horse beans, lentils, chick peas or garbanzos, and many more.

In the bean genus (*phaseolus*), there are many varieties and species. *Phaseolus vulgaris* includes string beans, navy, kidney, and many others. The Chinese mung bean, (*P. aureus*) about the size of an air rifle shot, and green, is sprouted for bean sprouts. (You can buy them canned in many grocery stores.) *Phaseolus limensis* is the lima bean, and there are still others.

Many of our forage crops belong here, including clovers, sweet clover, alfalfa, and soy bean. Garden flowers are well represented. Sweet peas and lupine are examples. The fragrant vine, wisteria, is another relative, and so are numerous shrubs, including *Caragena*. Others are trees such as the black and honey locusts, the lovely redbud or Judas tree, and the Kentucky coffee bean. In fact, as we will learn in the chapter on the fine woods, the bean family furnishes about one-fourth of the most beautiful woods in the world, by far the most important source. All the acacias and rosewoods belong here.

The roots of a legume, *Glycyrrhiza glabra*, native to the Mediterranean, furnish the licorice of commerce. Most people confuse licorice with anise and candies flavored with either are often colored black, but anise is a member of the next family we will discuss, the Umbelliferae.

Figure 3

Umbellifer Inflorescence
Wild Carrot

Members of the Umbelliferae, the carrot family, can usually be recognized rather easily by the great number of small flowers arranged in an umbrella-shaped manner on the end of the flower stalks. Queen Anne's lace, or wild carrot, is a familiar example. It is really wild carrot; man has bred up our cultivated golden carrots from these thin, light yellow, fibrous roots. The same is true for cultivated and wild parsnip. If you want to take a lens to the small flowers, they have five sepals, five petals and five stamens, but the "umbrellas" are usually sufficient. Celery belongs in this group, and a whole row of plants used for flavoring — dill, parsley, caraway, coriander, fennel, and others. There is also a strain of deadly poison in the family, and some of the poisonous species are discussed in the chapter "Borgias of the Plant World."

There are three closely related plant families that are not too difficult to recognize. Their floral parts tend to be in threes. One of these, the Liliaceae, usually has no sepals, six petals (or three sepals and three petals), six stamens, and a three-pointed pistil, with three divisions to the ovary. In the vegetable garden we find onion, chives, garlic, leeks (species of Allium) and asparagus (*Asparagus officinale*). There is another edible relative, native to the Canary Island, the climbing butcher's broom, *Semele androgyna*. There are several ornamental relatives of the garden asparagus, for example the fern asparagus (*a. plumosus*) and the *Asparagus sprengeri*, used much for foliage by florists. The briary, green-stemmed vine called catbriar belongs here. The genus, rather a large one, is *Smilax*, and there are several members that are not briary.

The number of cultivated and wild flowers in the lily family is enormous. Other than the many lilies themselves, there are *Aloe*, *Trillium*, *Yucca*, *Clintonia*, Solomon's seal, false Solomon's seal, lily of the valley, tulip, hyacinth, grape hyacinth, day lily (*Hemerocallis*), *Erythronium* (some of them cultivated, but including the wildling we call spotted adder's tongue), and a host of others. The Joshua trees of the deserts in the southwest show us that lilies can be trees.

The iris family (*Iridaceae*) is closely related. For the beginner, detailed technical differentiation is not too important. Many of them have leaves that characteristically clasp one another in a fanlike manner, as in *Iris, Gladiolus, Tigridia*, the small-flowered yellow star grass and blue-eyed grass and others. Crocus belongs here too.

The third of these closely related families, the *Amaryllidaceae*, has one easily recognizable characteristic: the flower buds are enclosed in a sheath — the remains are attached at the base of the flower after it opens. Watch for it in *Narcissus,* daffodil, *Amaryllis,* nerine lily, and many more.

All three of the above families are worldwide in distribution, and learning to recognize the members will start you on the road to the identification of many flowers. Before we leave them, the beginner should be made aware that there are several not-too-far-distantly related flowers that are not in these three families. Examples that come to mind at the moment are *Canna* and spiderwort (*Tradescantia*).

The members of the rose family *Rosaceae* are rather easy to recognize. There are a great many of them, they are widely distributed over the world, and many are of great importance. Basically the floral count is five sepals, five petals, many stamens, and pistils varying with the manner of fruiting. Thus the plums and cherries, with a single seed, have a single pistil. Apple and pear, with five seed compartments, have a five-pointed pistil. Strawberries and raspberries, as we would expect, have many pistils.

The five-count, though general, has exceptions. Jetbead, for example, goes to four. It is a rather common shrub. As in the case of many other cultivated flowers, man has selected variants with many petals. The rose is an example.

The bulk of the fruits in temperate regions belong here — apples, pears, peaches, plums, cherries, quince, apricots, juneberries, raspberries, blackberries, loganberries, strawberries, etc. There are many more lacking edible fruits, including spireas, the several herbaceous and shrubby cinquefoils (the name means five leafed, because many of them have leaves divided into five leaflets), thorn apples, firethorn, jet bead, *Kerria,* etc. Probably half of our ornamental shrubs are in Rosaceae.

Another large family is the *Compositae*. The word means "placed together," and refers to the fact that in members of this family a great many individual flowers are placed on a single receptacle. Familiar examples are dandelion and sunflower. Obviously, with so many flowers placed in close proximity, bees and other pollinating insects can transfer a lot of pollen in a hurry. In flowers like *Cosmos,* sunflower, and aster, the outer petals, called ray petals, are sterile (lack reproductive organs) and are used strictly for advertising, to attract bees, butterflies, and other pollinating insects.

Some botanists divide this family into sub-families, and there is considerable justification for this. However, that is for the professional, and need not concern the beginner. In the vegetable garden, lettuce in its many forms, chicory, endive, salsify or oyster plant, cultivated for its root, are in the Compositae. The globe artichoke bears an odd-looking green bud, developed by man through cultivation, apparently from *Cynara cardunculus,* the cardoon from the Mediterranean region. However, it has become so modified that it is now classed as a separate species, *Cynara Scolymus.* The bud, which vaguely resembles a globular pine cone is offered for sale in large city markets in the United States, especially where the population includes many people of Mediterranan origin. The base of the bracts is the edible part. The thickened leaf stalks and root of the cardoon are also used for food, especially in southern Europe.

Europeans found the natives of the New World growing a sunflower species, *Hellianthus tuberosus,* for its edible tubers. Italians began to cultivate it, and called it *girasole,* which means, in Italian, that it turns toward the sun — as we would expect a sunflower to do. English-speaking people corrupted *girasole* to Jerusalem, and Jerusalem artichoke it has remained in the English language ever since, although it has no connection at all with Jerusalem. (Man does love to twist names around. You should hear what he has done to plant names in Australia. One of the mahogany relatives there, for example, is called "maple silkwood.")

A great many of our cultivated flowers are in *Compositae.* A casual check through a recent Burpee catalog revealed that of ninety flower species offered for sale twenty-eight, or over thirty percent belong in this family. In addition to species previously mentioned, there are dahlia, zinnia, China asters, bachelor's button, chrysanthemum, gaillardia, marigold, and all the many daisies — indeed the daisy relatives form what might well be called the backbone of the mixed flower garden. The wild relatives run into a great number of genera and hundreds of species of universal distribution. Some of them in the tropics are trees. Others are bad weeds, as you will find in a later chapter.

Several of the Compositae are wind-pollinated, and so have no showy flowers. Ragweed is one of these — the hay-fever sufferer can vouch for the fact that it is wind-pollinated. *Artemisia* is another, and so is the sagebrush of the southwest.

As a family the *Cucurbitaceae* has members so easily recognized that no beginner will have much trouble with it. Cucumbers belong here, and so do pumpkins, squashes, and gourds. All melons are members of the family. These are discussed in some detail in the chapter, "Fruits of the World." There are several wild cucurbits scattered over the world, including the spiny-fruited, inedible wild cucumbers common in temperate United States. The vining habit is general through the family, although certain horticultural varieties do not vine much.

The next family we'll examine is the *Solanaceae*. The name indicates that members of the family like a lot of sun and, with a few exceptions, this is true. It is certainly a varied family, including annual and perennial herbs, shrubs, vines and, in the tropics, fair-sized trees. However, it is not a very hard family with which to become familiar. The floral count is five sepals, five petals, five stamens, one or more of which may be sterile and a single pistil. The petals are more or less fused together — the scientific term is "gamopetalous." Members of the family divide rather easily into two groups. The group furnishing our garden vegetables has fleshly fruits and rather flattish or cup-shaped flowers with five points or five divisions. In this group we have tomato, the many garden pepper varieties, potato, egg plant and ground cherry. Related to ground cherry is the very ornamental Chinese lantern plant, *Physalis alkekengi* with inflated, red-orange, balloonlike calyces, commonly used in winter bouquets and in florists' arrangements.

Members of the other section of the family have dry fruits and funnellike or hornlike flowers. Included are petunia, *Salpiglossis* or painted tongue, *Nicotiana,* and angel's trumpet. Many, if not most, of the flowers in this part of the family have a very heavy perfume. Tobacco is *Nicotiana tabacum,* although a few other *Nicotiana* species are used for tobacco also. Jimson weed belongs in this section. Several bad weeds are found in the family.

Not common to most backyard gardens, but still an important vegetable crop, is sweet potato in the *Convolvulaceae,* the morning-glory family. The name yam, occasionally applied to sweet potato varieties, is better applied to an unrelated tropical root vegetable. Floral count won't mean much for sweet potato because the conditions under which it is grown rarely result in flowering. However, most members of the family have funnelshaped flowers made up of five fused petals, a five-parted calyx, five stamens and a single pistil. All of them that you are apt to encounter are vines, although there are shrubby and even tree-like relatives. Besides the several morning-glory varieties and species, cypress vine, with its long, scarlet flowers and feathery leaves is often grown as an ornamental. Many wild morning-glories are bad weeds, especially European bindweed, as you'll see in the chapter on weeds.

If we cared to grow it, and many in the South do, we could plant okra, the green fruits of which are used in soups and other dishes. It is in the hollyhock family, the *Malvaceae,* where we also find cotton. The large genus *Malva* in this family includes the many mallow varieties. From the roots of one of them, the marshmallow, may be obtained a mucilaginous substance once used in making a confection. However, our present day marshmallows contain gelatin, rather than extract of marshmallow root, to give them their characteristic texture. There may be some of the pale-pink flowered marshmallows growing in a marshy area near your home. The red, fleshy, sour calyces of roselle of the Old World tropics are used in jellies and sauce.

Malvaceae is a very large family, worldwide in distribution, and is one of the easiest to recognize from the flowers. The count is five sepals, five petals, and single pistil which is surrounded by a great many stamens, *the filaments of which are fused to the pistil.* It is

Figure 4

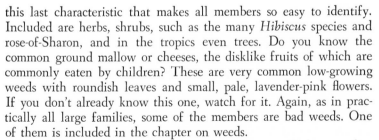

Arrangement of Stamens in a Flower
of the Family Malvaceae

this last characteristic that makes all members so easy to identify. Included are herbs, shrubs, such as the many *Hibiscus* species and rose-of-Sharon, and in the tropics even trees. Do you know the common ground mallow or cheeses, the disklike fruits of which are commonly eaten by children? These are very common low-growing weeds with roundish leaves and small, pale, lavender-pink flowers. If you don't already know this one, watch for it. Again, as in practically all large families, some of the members are bad weeds. One of them is included in the chapter on weeds.

If you have a large, old-fashioned garden, you'll have a few rhubarb plants, the acid leaf stems of which make such good pies and conserves. Rhubarb is in the enormous and widely distributed family, the *Polygonaceae,* and so is buckwheat. The flowers in this family are small, although in some species the floral masses are quite showy, as in the ornamental sometimes called kiss-me-over-the-garden-gate. However, there is an easy way to identify members of the family that any beginner can see. Do you recall the last time you pulled a rhubarb stem that there was a membrane at the base of the stem? All members of this family will have such a membrane more or less surrounding the stem at the base of each leaf stem or petiole. Watch for this membrane in such common weeds as smartweed, lady's thumb, dock (with the coffee-groundslike seeds on top in autumn), and the prostrate, dark green, wiry, dooryard knotweed that grows along trodden paths and edges of walks where nothing else will grow. All of these, and many more, are common weeds of wide distribution. The small tree called the sea grape, native to the Caribbean region, is described in the chapter, "Fruits of the World," while, in tropical America, palo Maria (Mary's tree) grows as tall and straight as a pine. When in flower, it is, depending on species, a mass of brilliant pinkish red, or a mass of shimmering gold.

The occurrence of such a membrane at the base of each leaf is not confined to family Polygonaceae, however. Leaves of many plants have protective scales, particularly in the cooler parts of the world, although in very few cases do they adhere to the stem once the leaf has expanded. In most cases they are soon shed, — examples: willows, maples, elms, magnolias, tulip trees, etc. There is one other family, however, in which these leaf scales or membranes do persist, and, if the flower can be examined, placement in family is certain. This is the *Araceae*, the Arum family. Here belong Jack-in-the-pulpit, skunk cabbage, calla lily, sweet flag, and a host of others. The "Jack" of Jack-in-the-pulpit is called, botanically, a spadix, and the "pulpit," a spathe. Not only are members of this family easily recognized, but they are of world-wide distribution. Many of our indoor ornamentals belong here, although in some cases flowering may not be too common under our conditions. Among those commonly grown indoors or in greenhouses are *Anthurium* (the spathes of which are often brilliantly colored — one of them scarlet, for example); *Caladium* ("Elephant Ear" — often planted in parks in the summer); *Dieffenbachia*, with large, mottled leaves; *Monstera*, with great, perforated and marginally cut leaves (in *Monstera deliciosa*, the spadix is edible; see "Fruits of the World"); Philodendron, which is a climber; and there are many more.

If you have an old-fashioned garden, you may have some plants of sage, mint, and marjoram in one corner. These mints (family *Labiatae*) are so easy to identify that the beginner can hardly fail to recognize them. The stems of all mints are square in cross section, and the leaves are opposite each other on the stems, each successive pair of leaves being at right angles to the preceding pair. The flowers are bilaterally symmetrical, which means that the right and left sides are the same. Most, and there are an enormous number, have a spicy odor, and for this reason many of them are used for spices. There are several, however, that do not have a spicy odor at all, including the common ornamental Coleus, grown for its colored foliage. (There is a sunflower species with a stem square in cross section. Be a bit careful here.)

The violet-pansy family (*Violaceae*) is easy. The flowers are bilaterally symmetrical, as are those of the mints, but have five separate petals, while the mints have tubular flowers. The pansy is a violet (*Viola tricolor*). Certain relatives in the tropics become trees.

The orchid family (*Orchidaceae*) is world wide and, with a few exceptions, very easily recognized. The flowers have three sepals which are often petal-like and three petals, the two lateral ones alike and the center one modified into a lip, either open or partly closed, as in lady slipper. When I was about ten years old I saw a spike of small, purple flowers growing in a swamp. I examined it, noticed that the petals were fringed and said to myself, "This will be purple fringed orchid." It was about ten years later that I found out I was correct. As there are more than sixteen thousand species in the world, once you recognize them, you will be able to put a lot of plants into family.

Equally easy to recognize are members of the grape family (Vitaceae). All species I know are vines. The five-leafed ivy or woodbine belongs here — the fruits certainly look like wild grapes. There is an ornamental relative, the porcelain berry, that has escaped from cultivation along our Eastern seaboard. The inedible fruits are beautifully colored in green, blue, and purple, and do look like porcelain. Unfortunately, they lose color on drying.

The last family here considered is large, and not as uniform as some of those previously considered, but once you get the feel of it, members are not hard to recognize. This is the Ericaceae. Most of them have rather thickish, leathery leavees, although the leaves of blueberry are not so much so. The leaves are arranged in the two-five spiral pattern on the stems, as described earlier in the chapter. The flowers have five sepals, five petals, five or ten stamens, and one pistil. The petals are fused into a cup or tube, or are somewhat saucer shaped, depending on species. Those with leathery leaves usually hold them through the winter. Several, other than blueberry, bear edible fruits, including huckleberry, cranberry, and wintergreen. Others, such as heather, trailing arbutus, mountain laurel, azalea, and rhododendron, are dry fruited.

Don't be too sure that anything with leathery leaves is in Ericaceae. Holly, in Aquifoliaceae, and members of the genus *Mahonia* in Berberidaceae are a couple of examples to the point.

Do I expect too much when I suggest that you can place many plants in family on the basis of these few notes? Recently, in a final exam in biology, I placed a sprig of salal with no flowers in a container of water with a note: "Five points extra credit. Put it in family." Fifty high-school students, none of whom had ever before seen salal, took the exam, and forty of them got it right. They had not had over fifteen minutes indoctrination on the family, the Ericaceae.

And so, with these few families in mind, you are well on your way toward becoming more familiar with plants.

SCIENTIFIC NAMES AND FAMILIES FOR FAIRLY COMMON PLANTS*

Plant	Scientific Name	Family
Alfalfa	*Medicage sativa*	Leguminosae
Artichoke, Globe	*Cynara cardunculus*	Compositae
Artichoke, Jerusalem	*Helianthus tuberosus*	Compositae
Asparagus	*Asparagus officinalis*	Liliaceae
Aster	*Aster* spp.	Compositae
Aster, China	*Callistephus chinensis*	Compositae
Bamboo	*Bambusa* spp.	Gramineae
Barley	*Hordeum vulgare*	Gramineae
Bachelor's Button	*Centaurea cyanus*	Compositae
Bean, Mung	*Phaseolus aureus*	Leguminosae
Bean (String, Navy, Kidney)	*Phaseolus vulgaris*	Leguminosae
Beet	*Beta vulgaris*	Chenopodiaceae
Broccoli	*Brassica oleracea* var. *botrytis*	Cruciferae
Brussels Sprouts	*Brassica oleracea* var. *gemmifera*	Cruciferae
Buckwheat	*Fagopyrum esculentum*	Polygonaceae
Cabbage	*Brassica oleracea* var. *capitata*	Cruciferae

*Spices, herbs, and condiments are listed at the end of Chapter 10. Fruits are listed at the end of Chapter 9. Trees are discussed in Chapter 20.

Plant	Scientific Name	Family
Chinese Cabbage, Pak-Choi	Brassica chinensis	Cruciferae
Carrot	Daucus carota var. sativa	Umbelliferae
Cauliflower	Brassica oleracea var. botrytis	Cruciferae
Celery	Apium graveolens var. dulce	Umbelliferae
Celery Cabbage, Pe-Tsai	Brassica pekinensis	Cruciferae
Chickpea	Cicer arietinum	Leguminosae
Clover, Common	Trifolium spp.	Leguminosae
Clover, Sweet	Melilotus spp.	Leguminosae
Columbine	Aquilegia hybrids	Ranunculaceae
Corn, Maize	Zea mays	Graminae
Cosmos	Cosmos bipinnatus and other species	Compositae
Cotton	Gossypium hirsutum and other species	Malvaceae
Cow Pea	Vigna sinensis	Leguminosae
Cucumber	Cucumis sativus	Cucurbitaceae
Daffodil	Narcissus Pseudo — Narcissus	Amaryllidaceae
Dandelion	Taraxacum officinale	Compositae
Delphinum	Delphinium spp. and hybrids	Ranunculaceae
Egg Plant	Solanum Melongena	Solanaceae
Endive	Cichorium Endivia	Compositae
Garbanzo	Cicer arietinum	Leguminosae
Geranium	Pelargonium spp. and hybrids	Geraniaceae
Gourd	Cucurbita spp. and Lagenaria spp.	Cucurbitaceae
Ground Cherry	Physalis pruinosa and other species	Solanaceae
Hollyhock	Althea rosea and A. ficifolia (with indented leaves)	Malvaceae
Hyacinth	Hyacinthus spp.	Liliaceae
Iris	Iris spp.	Iridaceae
Kale	Brassica oleracea var. acephala	Cruciferae
Kohlrabi	Brassica caulorapa	Cruciferae
Larkspur, see Delphinium		
Leek	Allium Porrum	Lilaceae
Lettuce	Lactuca sativa	Compositae
Lilac	Syringa vulgaris and other species	Oleaceae

Plant	Scientific Name	Family
Lily	*Lilium* spp.	Liliaceae
Marigold, Garden	*Tagetes erecta*	Compositae
Narcissus	*Narcissus spp.*	Amaryllidaceae
Oats	*Avena sativa*	Graminae
Okra	*Hibiscus esculenta*	Malvaceae
Onion	*Allium Cepa* and other species	Liliaceae
Pansy	*Viola tricolor*	Violaceae
Parsnip	*Pastinaca sativa*	Umbelliferae
Pea, Garden	*Pisum sativum*	Leguminosae
Pea, Sweet	*Lathyrus odoratus*	Leguminosae
Pepper, Sweet	*Capsicum frutescens*	Solanaceae
Peony	*Paeonia* spp. especially *P. albiflora* and *P. suffruticosa* and hybrids	Ranunculaceae
Petunia	*Petunia hybrida* (commonly grown garden petunia)	Solanaceae
Poppy	*Papaver* spp.	Papaveraceae
Potato	*Solanum tuberosum*	Solanaceae
Potato, Sweet	*Ipomoea Batatus*	Convolvulaceae
Pumpkin	*Cucurbita Pepo*	Cucurbitaceae
Radish	*Raphanus sativus,* etc.	Cruciferae
Rhubarb, Pie Plant	*Rheum Rhaponticum*	Polygonacae
Rice	*Oryza sativa*	Graminae
Rose	*Rosa* spp. and hybrids	Rosaceae
Rutabaga	*Brassica Napobrassica*	Cruciferae
Rye	*Secale cereale*	Graminae
Snapdragon	*Antirrhinum majus*	Scrophulariaceae
Spinach	*Spinacia oleracea*	Chenopodiaceae
Squash	*Cucurbita maxima, C. moschata*	Cucurbitaceae
Tobacco	*Nicotiana tabacum*	Solanaceae
Tomato	*Lycopersicon esculentum*	Solanaceae
Tulip	*Tulipa Gesneriana* and other species	Liliaceae
Turnip	*Brassica Rapa*	Cruciferae
Verbena	*Verbena* hybrids	Verbenaceae
Violet	*Viola* spp. (Pansy is *Viola tricolor*)	Violaceae
Wheat	*Triticum aestivum*	Graminae
Zinnia	*Zinnia elegans*	Compositae

CHAPTER 4

The Struggle to Survive

EVERY organism attempts to stay alive long enough to reproduce itself. If all the individuals of a single kind are unsuccessful in producing offspring, the race becomes extinct. This has happened many times in the past with both plants and animals. Plants that have survived are especially well constructed to maintain themselves in condition to reproduce their kind. Exceptions are many plants cultivated by man that depend on him for their continued existence.

Weeds may overwhelm our gardens, or trees obscure our view within a season; there appears to be no hindrance to their development. Yet every seedling enters life in competition with other plants for water, sunlight, and soil nutrients. If growth is too dense, lack of air circulation may encourage disease organisms that kill seedlings. A week of rainy weather may deprive young roots of oxygen and cause them to die. Moreover, plants may be eaten by all sorts of animals, from slugs, mites, and insects up to mammals. For this reason plants have, through the ages, evolved many methods of defense.

The silent but deadly battle for existence goes on all around us. Step out of the door and look at the weeds that thrive in the lawn — dandelions, plantain, chicory, and others. The rosette of leaves that some of these spread to the sunlight shades out the established grasses. Dandelion and chicory send tap roots deep into the soil to obtain water and nutrients from below the layers tapped by the shallow-feeding grasses, while the fibrous plantain roots compete successfully with grass.

All living things carry on their vital processes with the aid of water; without water no plant — or animal — can develop. The supply presents no problem to the many aquatic microscopic plants, pond scums, seaweeds, or to such seed plants as water-hyacinths and watercress, unless their wet habitat dries up. Plants that grow in the soil, however, must obtain their water from the soil, and with it certain essential minerals, besides compounds of sulfur, phosphorus, and nitrogen. In the tropics, many orchids and bromeliads spend their lives attached to trees. These must obtain water from the air — from rain or dew. Their minerals and other essentials they must obtain from the dust of the air or from the dead bark of the trees upon which they grow. When we see Spanish moss growing on power lines in the South, we should marvel at the efficiency of a plant that can thrive under such conditions.

If water is available, a plant still has the problem of maintaining its supply close to the proper level. Much water is lost from leaves by evaporation. For plants living in rain forests or swamps this may present no problem, but for dry-region dwellers or neglected garden plants the problem can be severe. If a plant continues to lose more water than it can absorb, it wilts and eventually dies. To conserve water, plants have developed many devices, such as a thick, waxy leaf cuticle, a heavy layer of fuzz, mechanisms to close the holes in the leaves (stomata) through which carbon dioxide is absorbed and oxygen released, or mechanisms that enable the leaves to roll up when moisture must be conserved. Note this last if you pass a corn field on a hot day or a rhododendron on a dry cold winter day.

In Northern regions winter is a period of drought for trees and shrubs, because the means by which water is absorbed from the soil and carried through the plant can no longer function efficiently. For this reason the leaves are commonly dropped. Plants like holly and rhododendron that retain their leaves through winter have a waxy coating and thick cuticle on the leaves to conserve moisture. In the tropics many trees drop their leaves during the dry season, which is often referred to as "winter" for this reason.

In regions where water supply is extremely critical, as in the desert, many plants dispense with leaves and carry on photosynthesis on fleshy green stems. Cacti on the desert, for instance, lack leaves, but the cactus *Pereskia,* which grows as a small tree in parts of tropical America where water is reasonably abundant, does have true leaves.

We commonly say that a plant or animal develops modifications that enable it more successfully to compete — as though the plant or animal behaved intelligently. This isn't the way it works at all. Here is the real explanation. Between individuals of any one species we may observe small differences. Some of these may affect the individual's chances for survival, rendering it more (or less) able to compete. Those that are more able survive and reproduce, while those less able to compete may die without reproducing. Thus there is a constant tendency for more successful individuals to pass along to their offspring those characteristics upon which their success depends. For example, if a plant has thorns, while a second plant of the same kind lacks thorns, the second plant may be browsed to extinction. Similarly, the predatory animal that is too weak, too slow, or too stupid to capture and kill some other animal will starve to death and leave no offspring. For all living things, life is for those that can compete; death for those that cannot.

Leonardo da Vinci was the first, or one of the first, to point out that leaves of trees are, as a general rule, arranged to catch as much sunlight as possible. However, some plants become adapted to lower light intensity and take their place beneath the shade of the canopy trees. In the struggle for light, many plants attach themselves to the trunks and branches of the tall jungle trees. Such plants are called "epiphytes," meaning "growing on another plan." We find representatives of many different plant families doing this — ferns, mosses, orchids, bromeliads (which are relatives of pineapple), and others. It is probable that one could find as many as fifty different kinds of epiphytes growing on a single giant tropical tree.

Vines, springing either from the forest floor or from seeds sprouting on the trunks of trees, grow quickly to the tops of trees in their search for light. The great number of vines is a sight that makes a deep impression on anyone first visiting a tropical jungle. Many of these vines are especially adapted to resist stress during tropical storms that whip the canopy trees from side to side. They have stems that grow in a zigzag pattern, allowing them to lengthen without breaking.

Vines in several families go one step further and strangle the tree on which they are growing. The strangler fig, related to mulberry, family Moraceae, is infamous in this respect. The seed sprouts on the trunk of a tree and the young plant sends roots down into the soil, while the top grows upward to the forest canopy. Then modified roots encompass the tree, and actually constrict and kill it. Finally the fig will have entirely covered the tree on which it is growing, and the supporting tree rots away enclosed by the strangler. *Clusia rosea,* a member of a tropical family, the Guttiferae, grows in a similar manner, although there appears to be some disagreement among authorities whether the tree will be killed.

Certainly a number of *Clusia* species merely cling to another tree. However, the name, "matapalo" (tree killer) applied to *Clusia rosea* would indicate that the natives have seen it kill trees — and

Figure 5

A Matapalo (Tree Killer) Strangling a Tree in South America
From: Timbers of the New World, *by Samuel J. Record and Robert W. Hess. Yale University Press. Used by permission.*

this name is common through northern South America, Central America, and several of the islands of the West Indies. The illustration would indicate that it certainly wouldn't be particularly beneficial to a tree. (Another interesting common name in French Guiana is "mille-pieds," which is our word millipede, a name suggested by the many rootlike holdfasts.) Scientists in New Zealand have observed similar growth in members of the violet, dogwood, and ginseng families, as well as in members of the tropical family Cunoniaceae. Thus it is obvious that many different plants have successfully used this method for reaching sunlight.

Coming back to more familiar surroundings, remember the last thick patch of wild raspberries you visited? The raspberries send up suckers all around the edge of the patch, and these form such a heavy canopy as to shade out much of the competition. The beech tree has a different problem. Because of its manner of growth, it would be disadvantageous to have too many beech trees too close together. The leaves of the beech, when they fall to the ground, release a chemical that prevents the sprouting of beech seeds beneath the parent tree. This is chemical warfare, and it is very common in the plant world. The drug penicillin, for example, is merely a chemical used by the fungus *Penicillium notatum* to keep other organisms at a distance. Penicillin just happens to be tolerated by most human beings in amounts that will kill bacteria. Penicillin is an antibiotic. All antibiotics are of this nature and, as we would expect, there are many that are too poisonous to human beings to be useful in medicine.

In the deserts of southwestern United States a daisylike plant called brittlebush has leaves that contain a chemical that makes it impossible for seeds of other plants to germinate in the soil near it. The toxic substance of the leaves has been identified as 3-acetyl-6-methoxy-benzaldehyde. You may be familiar with the parent compound, benzaldehyde or oil of bitter almonds. Another daisy relative that grows in the desert, guayule, employs cinnamic acid for the same purpose. Creosote bush also secretes a poisonous chemical to control competition. The use of chemicals by these plants, however, is related to competition for the meager water supply available on the desert. It has been shown, in the case of the creosote bush at least, that heavy rains will leach the poisonous substance from the soil around the plant to such an extent that seeds *will* germinate.

The leaves and hulls of black walnut are known to cause injury to several plants, and it has been suggested that the chemical, juglone, found in black walnut, may be the toxic substance. The ginkgo tree has been shown to protect itself from fungal attack by use of chemicals such as alpha hexenal. Chemical warfare between plants is indeed so general that one investigator in California reported the leaves of about half of the woody species tested were poison to one or more test plants.

Plants must provide for periods unfavorable to growth —for winter or for dry periods. Annuals die at the end of their season, but before they die they have provided the new plant, contained as an embryo in the seed, with sufficient food to start it on its way. Perennials store food in their trunks, in the roots, or in underground stems, to enable them to get an early start when conditions are again favorable for growth. We use these stored foods when we tap a maple for its sap, or gather carrots, turnips, beets, or potatoes.

Finally, each plant must provide for the dissemination of its offspring. While a part of this story is told in later chapters, we should be aware of the many devices employed by plants to insure that their seeds, or spores in the case of spore plants, are spread far and wide. Scattering movements depending on internal stresses (springlike devices) are commonly used. For example, the pods of the ordinary garden bean and many of its relatives explode when dry. So do the seed capsules of oxalis[1] and violet. Although I had my first introduction to jewelweed, or touch-me-not, years ago, I still start a bit when its mature seed capsules snap open between my fingers. This plant grows in marshy areas or even in creeks. You'll recognize it by its yellow or orange flowers that somewhat resemble small nasturtiums. The ripe seed pods of the sandbox tree of the South American tropics explode violently, with a sound like firecrackers. One of my friends had one of these in a cigar box. When it exploded, it blew the box to pieces. Sometime when you are walking through North American woodlands, you may hear the seed capsules of the shrubby tree, witch hazel, pop as they forcibly discharge their seeds.

Ferns developed very efficient mechanisms for spore dispersal millions of years ago. Their microscopic spores do the same for ferns as seeds do for the higher plants. The spores of most species are contained in a small sac which is comparable to a seed capsule. When the spores are mature, an attached band that resembles a curved spinal column bends backward until it ruptures the mem-

---

[1]Oxalis is the common weed with leaves resembling clover leaves, but with a pleasant, sour taste. The flowers are yellow, pink, or occasionally white, depending on the species.

brane that contains the spores. The same device then plunges forward, scattering the spores. If you fill your hand with pebbles, place it palm upward above your shoulder, and then whip your arm forward, you will have duplicated the action exactly.

Figure 6

Fern Spore Dispersal

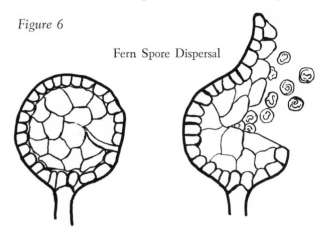

Many fungi hurl their spores into the air forcibly. I have seen such spore discharge in a fungus found in corn cobs, *Nigrospora oryzae.* Although the organism is microscopic in structure, it can hurl spores at least an inch into the air. In proportion to size, a six-foot man similarly propelled would be hurled to a height of nearly two miles. It is not difficult to find bird's nest fungi in almost any of our wooded areas. These drab grayish structures, about a half-inch or less across, look like small birds' nests, with a cluster of "eggs" at the bottom. These "eggs," which contain the spores of the fungus, may be hurled ten feet into the air.

How do these movements originate? There are several ways. For example, the living jelly, called protoplasm, contained in the cells of the plants, may exert pressure in such a manner as to result in movement, or the cell may simply become so inflated with water (hydrostatic pressure) that a forcible discharge results, or the drying of the plant tissues may produce sufficient tensions to result in an explosion.

Many wild fruits are just the right size for a bird to swallow, but the seeds are too hard to be digested. Thus wild cherries, wild grapes, raspberries, and many others have their seeds spread far and wide. This is the reason that many plants bear edible, fleshy fruits. Mistletoe, as you may know, grows as a semi-parasite on tree limbs.

Its berries are mucilaginous, and a bird eating them will commonly attempt to clean his bill by wiping it on a tree limb. In so doing he will often leave seeds on the limb; thus a new mistletoe plant may be started.

Seed (and spore) dispersal by the wind is very common. My garage at the moment is well provided with the heads of witch grass and of lace grass, whose seeds are scattered as these tumbling heads are blown about. This is an example of convergent evolution — a means of seed dispersal so successful that two unrelated grasses have come to resemble each other so closely that the casual observer would never notice that they are different species. There are many other "tumble" weeds in different parts of the world, the shape of which enables them to be rolled by the wind when they break free at maturity.

Winged seeds are very common. We find them in the elms, birches, basswoods, and maples. The shape of the maple seeds is almost exactly duplicated by certain trees in the bean family in South America — the genus *Macherium* — and by many members of the Asiatic family the Dipterocarpaceae. (The family name of the latter means a fruit with two wings.) As for seeds spread by means of a parachute of fluff, this is used by plants in an enormous number of families, plants such as dandelions, cattail, milkweed, dogbane, willow, poplar, certain sedges, and so on.

It is very clear, in dealing with plants, that we are studying organisms living under conditions of intense competition with many adaptations developed through the ages to stay alive, to reproduce, and to disseminate their offspring.

CHAPTER 5

Plants Are Far Travelers

PLANTS have been carried from one part of the world to another since long before the dawn of recorded history. The Swiss Lake Dwellers, a prehistoric Stone Age people of around 5,000 years ago, built their dwellings on piles over the shallow waters at the edges of certain lakes in the land that is now Switzerland. Doubtless this mode of life helped in procuring fish for food, disposing of garbage and sewage, and gaining a bit of a head start in the event of enemy attack. It also permitted the preservation of evidence concerning their housekeeping. If the lake-dwelling housewife accidently burned the dinner and dumped the results in the lake, evidence of what she had been cooking would be well preserved for present-day investigation.

Scientists have found such preserved material at sites of these ancient lake dwellings and have sufficient evidence to know that these people ate plums from the blackthorn and grew a species of perennial flax. Both of these were native to the region. They also grew apples. The Lake Dwellers had, in fact, learned to dry apples. They grew the common garden pea. Apples may have originated in or near the province of Chilan in Persia, while the garden pea probably originated in Asia, although some authorities say Abyssinia. The garden pea may be the most ancient of our cultivated vegetables. There are no wild forms of it in existence, although there are some close relatives.

It is often difficult for botanists to determine with certainty the original home of cultivated plants. In deciding, all available evidence is carefully weighed, including present distribution of wild ancestors or their relatives. Ancient records or artifacts often help considerably. New World pottery, for example, was frequently decorated with maize designs.

Many of our present-day plants were cultivated by the ancient Egyptians. Wheat and barley have both been found in the tombs

45

of the great Pharaohs. The Egyptians also cultivated the watermelon, which grows even today in its wild state in equatorial Africa. There are two wild forms, one sweet and one bitter. David Livingstone, the great missionary, saw both forms growing in the Kalahari Desert following heavy rains in 1857.

If a plant has been recently introduced to a new part of the world, names for it will usually be recognizably alike in different languages. If widely cultivated since ancient times, different peoples will have different names for the same plant. The fact that there are a great many common names for the watermelon among the several language groups in the Mediterranean region points to the antiquity of its cultivation. Western Asia received the watermelon early in the history of man, but it didn't reach China until the second century B.C. The Himalayas were a strong barrier to exchange of products through overland trade.

Both the ancient Greeks and Egyptians grew the common onion, which probably originated in Middle Asia. The exact place of origin is not certain because no wild form exists, although there are many wild relatives of it. The onion seems to have been distributed over the Mediterranean region from Western Asia. The ancient Egyptians considered one variety so fine that it was accorded divine honors. This idea was vastly amusing to the Romans who conquered Egypt, and one Roman suggested that it was so honored because "it smelled to high heaven." Designs depicting the onion were frequently carved on the ancient Egyptian monuments. Herodotus tells that in his time there were inscriptions on the Great Pyramid recording the sums spent for the onions, radishes, and garlics used to feed the builders of the pyramid. Oddly enough, the garlic is not pictured on the Egyptian monuments, probably because it was considered unclean — good to eat, but not worthy of such dignity. Again we can logically deduce that garlic has been cultivated since ancient times by the multiplicity of names for it among different peoples. Garlic may have come from the desert of the Kirghis of Sungari or near it, although no one knows exactly where it did originate. The Mongols probably brought it to China. Earliest records there date back to around 100-200 B.C.

The Bible is the source of information on some of the food plants of ancient Egypt. After Moses liberated the Jews from their Egyptian bondage, they did not find the Promised Land as soon as they had hoped. They were not happy about it and complained bitterly, as we may read in Numbers 11:5 — "We remember the fish, which we did eat in Egypt freely; the cucumbers and the melons, and the leeks, and the onions, and the garlick." And again we read in Numbers 20:5 — "And wherefore have ye made us to come up out of Egypt, to bring us in unto this evil place? it is no place of seed, or of figs, or of vines, or of pomegranates; neither is there any water to drink." (This sounds much like people of today.)

Flax was a common crop with the ancient Egyptians. Their mummies were wrapped in cloth made of flax fibre. The Hebrews also used it, but its use is more ancient still. The ancient Celts grew it, and it has long been used in India. The perennial flax, which we have already mentioned in connection with the Swiss Lake Dwellers, was also widely grown in very early times. The prehistoric dwellers of Lombardy, who appear to have inhabited Europe prior to the Aryan conquest, grew perennial flax. The use of the two species for fiber seems to have resulted from independent discovery.

The annual flax grown by the Egyptians, Celts, Hebrews, and ancient inhabitants of India seems to be of Asiatic origin. It is well represented on the Egyptian monuments; and Unger, a German botanist, has identified flax seed capsules taken from monuments dating back to around 1400 B.C. Flax has been found in a Chaldean tomb of even more ancient date, long before the time of Babylon. There is considerable evidence that this crop was carried from place to place by many of the ancient peoples at many times and very early.

As the annual flax became more widely cultivated, it replaced the perennial flax as a fiber crop in Europe. This replacement of one crop by another and better crop has been going on throughout the history of mankind and still continues.

Lettuce, which appears to have originated in the interior of Asia Minor, is also of ancient cultivation. It was well known to the Greeks and Romans. It was common on Persian tables at least six hundred years before Christ. However, it did not reach China until sometime before the fifth century, probably, as in the case of the watermelon, barred by the towering Himalayas and the vast reaches of the mid-Asiatic hinterlands.

The barriers that delayed introduction of crop plants to China were equally effective in the opposite direction. For example, most citrus fruits seem to have originated in China, although the lemon may have first been grown in northern Burma or nearby India. However, citrus cultivation in the Middle East and the Mediterranean region is, from the historical standpoint, comparatively recent.

The wild ancestor of cabbage, cauliflower, broccoli, kohlrabi, kale, collards, and Brussels sprouts — rock cress or cliff cabbage (*Brassica oleracea*) — is still common near the seashores of Europe and North Africa and was eaten by primitive people at least four thousand years ago — and probably ages before that. It was apparently in cultivation before the Aryan conquest. How far it has come since that time, with all of its highly bred forms and varieties! Plato mentions cabbage in his *Republic;* and Theophrastus, in his *Enquiry Into Plants,* written in 350 B.C., mentions smooth, wrinkled, and red cabbage and kale. These were loose-headed forms, adapted to warmer parts of the world. The hard-headed cabbages we now grow were developed in middle Europe, probably after A.D. 800. On the other hand, broccoli and cauliflower were both grown by the Romans. We have Roman records mentioning cauliflower that date back to around 600 B.C. The most recently developed plants of this group are kohlrabi and Brussels sprouts, which seemingly were developed in the cooler parts of Europe not over five hundred years ago.

The Chinese or celery cabbage is *Brassica pekinensis.* The nonheading relative, pak-choi, is *B. chinensis.* Both of the latter are mentioned in the *Ki Han,* the earliest known Chinese book on plants, written during the Chin Dynasty, A.D. 290-307.

The common "Irish" or white potato is of ancient cultivation in South America, having been grown along the west coast from south Chile and the Island of Chiloe to the highlands of Columbia since long before the arrival of the white man. Two species were grown: our common potato, suited to culture in the lowlands, and another species adapted to culture in the mountains. Probably both were derived from a common wild ancestor in Peru. However, the potato was not known to the aborigines of Brazil and the Guianas. Possibly its culture there was blocked by climate or disease, more probably the latter.

Gerard, an English botanist of the sixteenth century, says that he received from Virginia a potato plant which he cultivated in his garden. An illustration in which he is shown holding a flowering stalk of this plant appears in his account. However, there is no evidence that the potato was really grown in the colonies before the Spanish had spread it pretty generally over Europe sometime before 1583. Possibly Gerard's potato came from some Spanish ship pillaged by Sir Walter Raleigh or some other English gentleman-pirate. It was probably first brought into cultivation in North America by a group of Irish settlers in Londonderry, New Hampshire, in 1719.

Wild relatives of the potato grow even to this day in the

Andes, but these are different species from the cultivated varieties. Probably the original home was the highlands of northern Chile. It seems doubtful that its natural home extended as far north as Peru.

The common potato, along with many other crop plants, is known as a cultigen, which means that, as a species, it is distinct from any wild relatives. Occasionally, even the genus is known only in cultivation, as with Indian corn. Muskmelons, which may have originated in northern India, garden peas, onions, sweet potatoes and lemons are other examples of cultigens. Many cultigens have become so dependent on cultivation that they would vanish from the earth rather quickly were man to become extinct.

The Indians of Mexico grew a plant for food which, according to the first white explorers, they called tomati, tomatl, tumatl or tomatos, each explorer reporting what he though he heard. Most of the wild forms and relatives are found on the western slopes of the Andes from Ecuador south through Peru and Bolivia. It was well established in several parts of the world before it came to North America. The Italians were growing it as a field crop by the middle 1700's. Records indicate that it came back across the Atlantic to North America near the beginning of the 1800's. However, there is good reason to believe that the tomato has come into cultivation rather recently, compared to many other important crop plants. There was some prejudice against it when the white man first began to grow it, because there are poisonous relatives, for example, the deadly nightshade. In many parts of North America small fruited forms called love apples were grown as ornamentals.

The related pepper plant (*Capsicum frutescens*) – the garden plant, not the source of black pepper – is also of South American origin. However, the garden pepper has long been used for food. In contrast to popular prejudice against the tomato, European physicians near the end of the sixteenth century recommended the pepper as a cure-all. Columbus brought it to Spain in 1493, and its culture spread rapidly over the whole world. Traces of peppers have been found in Peruvian ruins dating back at least as early as the time of Christ. Sweet peppers seem to have originated as a chance variant only about 150 years ago. All peppers, hot or sweet, are varieties of one species.

Celery is another plant brought into cultivation in comparatively recent times, historically speaking. The wild ancestor still grows in damp places along the coast of the Mediterranean down to Abyssinia and east to India. The plant, as we know it, has been in the process of improvement as a salad vegetable only since the middle 1700's, although it was used for flavoring and in medicine back in the times of the Greeks and Romans. Well into the beginning of our present century, celery was blanched by use of soil or boards placed aaginst the stalks, and only with the comparatively recent advent of such varieties as Pascal and Utah have such practices become obsolete. There are several poisonous relatives, including the "hemlock" drunk by Socrates, and this fact may have delayed its introduction into our gardens.

Most of the history of the human race is tied closely to the struggle for food. Wars, commerce, exploration, great migrations — practically all of them were at least associated with the desire for better living conditions in which food plants, pasturage, and other plant products played a dominant role. *Cargoes and Harvests* by D. C. Peattie (Appleton, 1926) deals with this phase of man's relations with plants. This excellent book, now long out of print, may be obtained through many libraries.

The fascinating story of the spice trade is recounted briefly in a later chapter, "Odor in Plants."

In the New World the history of the tribes long before the arrival of the white man was likewise tied to the struggle for food plants. Wild rice (*Zizania aquatica*) is a grass that grows in shallow water. The wild-rice beds of central Wisconsin were important sources of food for the natives since time out of mind. (The plant is not closely related to cultivated rice.) The tribes of the region fought many bloody wars for the possession of the wild-rice beds, with the Chippewas finally gaining the upper hand over the Sioux. Long after that, however, the Sioux still raided the rice beds whenever possible.

Wheat has been an Old World crop for ages, as has rice in the Orient. In fact, we can state categorically that the European-North African civilizations were founded on wheat, the Asiatic on rice, and those of the New World prior to the advent of the white man on maize. On the other hand, oats were only brought into cultivation about 1000 B.C., in Asia Minor, while rye, which was later to become such an important food for the poorer classes in Europe, came under cultivation in Central Asia about the time of Christ. Both oats and rye were probably taken into cultivation because they were common weeds in wheat fields — thus showing their amenability to domestication.

Columbus brought muskmelon seeds to the New World. The Indians planted them widely. By the time the first white men pushed across the Appalachians, they found the muskmelon and the peach growing as far north as Canada. John Bartram, an early American botanist, was of the opinion that while the apple was brought into America by Europeans, the peach was a native American fruit. After all, the peach grew wild all along the banks of the Mississippi in Bartram's time — about the middle 1700's — even as it does today. However, the peach was probably first brought to North America by the Spanish when they settled St. Augustine in 1565. Later they brought it to Santa Fe, New Mexico, when they settled there in 1605. The Indians soon spread it far and wide, up along the east coast and west of the Appalachians, always preceding the white settlers in their migrations.

Flowers also have their stories, parallel to those of our food crops. We always think of Holland when we think of tulips. The Dutch got them second-handed from Turkey, which in turn had gotten them from India. The Dutch call them *tulpen,* a corruption of the name for the colorful turbans (*dulband*) worn by the peoples of the East. The flower found conditions in Holland to its liking, and the Dutch began to cultivate and hybridize it intensively. The staid Dutchmen went slightly crazy over them. Prices for choice new varieties went to fantastic heights. Often the price of a single bulb would be so great that several investors would own shares in it. When the boom collapsed, as such booms do, many men were financially ruined.

Today, new and better plant varieties are still constantly being taken from one end of the earth to the other. Plants are still far travelers.

FOR FURTHER READING

Anderson, Alexander W., *How We Got Our Flowers;* Dover, 1966.

Camp, Wendell H.; Victor R. Boswell; John R. Magness, *The World in Your Garden;* The National Geographic Society, Washington, D. C.

Fairchild, David, *The World Was My Garden;* Charles Scribner's Sons, 1938.

Helback, Hans, "Domestication of Food Plants in the Old World," *Science,* August 14, 1959 (Vol. 130, #3372).

Hill, Albert F., *Economic Botany;* McGraw-Hill Book Company.

Kingdon-Ward, Frank, *Pilgrimage for Plants;* Taplinger, 1966.

Klose, Nelson, *America's Crop Heritage;* Iowa State University Press, 1950.

Schery, Robert W., *Plants for Man;* Prentice-Hall, Englewood Cliffs, N. J.

CHAPTER 6

The Fascinating Story of a Common Plant

HEN Christopher Columbus discovered the New World, he sent two sailors to explore the interior of Cuba. On returning, they reported that the natives were growing "a sort of grain they call maiz which was well-tasted, bak'd, dry'd, and made into flour"; so records a contemporary English translation of their report.

This was the first encounter between the people of the Old World and corn. Columbus himself spoke of passing through eighteen miles of maize fields. All the spices he hoped to find in the Indies, all the gold that the Spaniards wrested from the Aztecs and Incas fade into insignificance before the worth of this one plant.

In an almost incredibly short time, probably not much more than forty years after the discovery of the New World, corn had been taken to the far corners of the earth and was being grown wherever it could be grown. Today the culture of maize or corn extends from north latitude 58° in Canada and Russia to south latitude 40°, and from below sea level in the Caspian Plain to altitudes of more than twelve thousand feet in Peru. It is grown under the most varied climatic conditions, from regions in Siberia with less than ten inches of rainfall annually to regions where the annual rainfall exceeds two hundred inches. One explorer tells of finding it cultivated in parts of eastern Africa where the natives had never before seen white men. These natives had grown corn from time out of mind and could not tell how or where they first obtained it. Incidentally, they cooked it in iron kettles made in Pittsburgh, the very existence of which city, of course, was absolutely unknown to them. The kettles, obviously, had passed into the interior through barter from the coast.

No other crop exceeds maize in value in our country, and in the whole world only two crops, wheat and rice, are more important. If all the cornfields of the world were made into one huge field it would cover an area more than 300 miles wide and 1,000 miles long. The annual world crop exceeds five billion bushels.

When Columbus discovered the New World, the four types of corn (pop, flint, flour, and sweet) were all known and had long been cultivated, but included in these principal groups are an enormous number of varieties. By 1939 the Russian government had a collection of eight thousand varieties, important as source of genetic material in corn breeding; and it is probable that many others were not included in the collection. As to length of season, Gaspe flint (grown on the Gaspe Peninsula in Canada) and Cinquantino (grown in the Pyrenees Mountains of Spain) mature in sixty to seventy days. Some varieties grown in Columbia, on the other hand, require ten to eleven months to reach maturity. Varieties are grown with stalks less than two feet tall, while others have stalks twenty feet or more in height. Some pop corns have thumb-sized ears. On the other hand, a few years ago a Navaho Indian in New Mexico grew an ear eighteen inches in length. An enormous variety grown in the Jala Valley of Mexico produces ears which, with shucks still attached, measure three feet in length. The stalks of this variety are so strong that they are employed in building stockades for livestock.

Kernels vary greatly in size from that of a grain of wheat in certain pop corns to flour corns with kernels as large as a quarter. Shapes of kernels are also extremely variable and so is the color of the seeds. Although the more prosaic white man has settled upon yellow or white corn almost exclusively, the Indians grew it (and still do) in shades of blue, white, red, orange, gold, and yellow. There are even varieties with striped and spotted kernels.

The importance of corn in the economy of the American natives can hardly be overestimated. The great Mayan, Aztec and Inca civilizations were founded upon this one plant. In fact, there is no other native American plant upon which a great civilization could have been founded, with the possible exception of the Irish potato. Relics depicting corn are common, some of them probably older than the more ancient civilizations of Chimu, Nasca and Tiuahuanaco.

The plant entered extensively into Indian art. Pottery decorations commonly employed corn, often in conventionalized forms. In the native ceremonies, religious and otherwise, corn was likewise prominent. The Inca, which title was applied to the ruler of that civilization, would go forth amid great ceremony at planting time to the terraces of Cuzco and, with a golden pickaxe, would break the soil. At harvest time another ceremony took place, during which the Inca harvested the first ears. Kernels from ears thus grown and harvested under the hand of the great ruler were considered sacred and were distributed over the kingdom for ceremonial plantings.

Ceremonies corresponding in general to those practiced in ancient civilizations of the Old World were also common. Among many of the native peoples of the Americas, corn was buried with the dead to sustain them on their journey to the hereafter. During the Inca harvest period from May 22 to June 22, a special festival offered sacrifice to Mama Sara, the Maize Mother. Each family wrapped a small quantity of maize in a piece of the finest cloth they possessed and buried it in the fields. It was also customary at Cuzco for the Virgins of the Sun to offer maize bread to the Sun God.

Among the Aztecs a goddess, Cinteotl, who derived her name from the Aztec word for maize, corresponded to the Greek goddess Ceres, and it was customary to offer the first fruits of the maize harvest to her each year. Human sacrifice to "the long-haired mother" was also practiced among the Aztecs. During the festival celebrating the formation of the corn ears they danced a symbolic dance in which the women would shake out their black tresses in imitation of the silks of the maize plant. Each evening the dance continued for a period of eight days. A captive Indian maiden would take part. She was encouraged to dance with abandon, for it was thought that on her responses depended the effectiveness of the ceremonies. She was, of course, kept in darkness as to her eventual role in the drama. At the end of the last dance the warriors appeared on the scene. The women danced the solemn death dance, and the whole populace formed a procession to the teocalli (sacrificial altar). Here the victim, the captive maid, was slain and her heart cut out and offered to the maize mother.

When Captain John Smith brought his gentlemen adventurers to Jamestown, his colony soon fell on evil days. The harvest was not plentiful because there were too few laborers — in fact, there was no harvest at all. Captain Smith, however, learned from the Indians how to grow corn; he obtained enough of it from them to keep his men alive and then told each man to plant and care for an acre of it. The Plymouth colony under Captain Miles Standish was also said to have been saved by the wonderful new grain when Squanto, a friendly Indian, taught the Pilgrims how to plant the kernels, and how to fertilize the plantings with dead fish.

As the pioneers moved westward, corn was often the main source of food for themselves as well as their animals. American agriculture is founded more squarely on corn than on any other plant. As time goes on, our country will come, we hope, to give this noble grain its just due. In fact, the maize plant has been seriously proposed as a national emblem. The beautiful fountain piece, designed by Christian Petersen for the Iowa State University, with statues of an Indian woman planting corn seeds, nurturing the young plants, harvesting the ears, and suckling her child, shows what a wealth of beauty may be found in familiar things.

Maize, as we indicated before, is strictly a product of the New World and was absolutely unknown to the Old World prior to the coming of Columbus. However, the native tribes have only legends to tell us how they acquired it. The Quinche Indians of western Guatemala in their sacred book, the *Popol Vuh,* tell of four barbarians who guided the Quinches to "a most excellent land so full of good things where white and yellow maize did abound." One Mayan legend has man created from maize meal, while another tells of gods or godlike men who came among them and took away with them four of the Mayan chiefs, these later returning with "ears of yellow maize and white." People fascinated by the lost Atlantis legend have suggested that the plant may have been native to that supposedly sunken continent.

How and where and when did maize actually originate? What were its ancestors? No one has ever found a wild form of maize, but more of that later. One thing is certain, maize has been nurtured by man ever since it took anything like its present form, because this plant is unable to propagate itself. It even lacks the power of returning to a more primitive form that could exist in the wild state. If man were to vanish from the earth, maize would not survive him by more than two years.

De Candolle, one of the older authorities, concluded that damp, low-lying regions such as those of Paraguay, Guiana, Panama, and the Amazon, being unfavorable to annuals, would be less likely as the original home of maize than the more arid high ground of Mexico or Chile (or Peru?). This contention, he felt, is supported by the fact that the latter regions became heavily populated rather early, which would not be likely in the absence of some staple cereal. He then goes on to point out that the civilizations of Peru and Mexico apparently arose quite independently, with little or no contact with each other; and that because both civilizations were founded on corn, it is possible that it may have had some inter-

mediate point of origin. He accordingly suggests that the very ancient Chibcha peoples who dwelt on the table lands of Colombia,
near Bogota, may have been the first to cultivate it. For deductive
reasoning this is not bad, although the long periods of time involved and the relative speed with which valuable crop plants are
accepted and spread even among primitive peoples bring doubt to
the second part of his theory.

How long has maize been cultivated? The Mayan chronology traces
back to 3140 or 3400 B.C., and this was one of the civilizations
founded on maize. There is abundant evidence that it was grown
for food ages before that. Dr. Elsa Bargdoorn of Harvard and Miss
Margaret Wolfe of Radcliffe have identified fossil maize pollen
from a boring two hundred feet below Mexico City, estimated to
be sixty thousand years of age. Although some doubts have been
expressed as to the validity of this find, later studies have pretty
well confirmed that this was really maize pollen although it may
have been a wild or primitive form.

We know several relatives and near-relatives of maize. *Teosinte*
is commonly found growing wild in or near Mexican corn fields and
hybridizes easily with corn. *Tripsacum* also grows in Mexico and
is related but hybridizes less readily. There are five Asiatic genera,
including the common Job's tears that have been placed close to
maize by systematists, possibly somewhat arbitrarily. The relationship
between maize and sorghum does not appear to be too remote.
Both maize and bamboo have been hybridized with sugar cane
which would indicate a fairly close relationship among these plants.
However, several authorities have long contended that the ancestor

Figure 7

Primitive Maize Ears
(Bat Cave, Mexico)

(*Courtesy: Dr. Paul C. Mangelsdorf*)

of maize is maize. In other words, there has existed at some time in the past some grass from which our present-day maize was derived by a long process of selection and possibly some crossing with a closely related grass or grasses, such as teosinte.

Corn cobs about the size of strawberries have been found in Bat Cave in New Mexico. These, according to Dr. Paul C. Mangelsdorf of Harvard, are definitely corn cobs. More recently many caves in Mexico which in the distant past were used for human habitations have been investigated. While all of these have yielded corn cobs and other maize tissues, these become more primitive and smaller in the deeper layers. A series of caves in the rather arid Tehuacan Valley, south and east of Mexico City, have yielded by far the richest evidence. Some of the most ancient cobs found there are scarcely cobs at all, and are only a little over an inch long.

Previously, Mangelsdorf and Reeves had done extensive breeding work in attempts to get back to a form similar to wild maize. On the basis of this work and the findings in the caves they concluded that the wild form would have the seeds at least partly enclosed in the bractlike glumes common to other grasses, and that the kernels would be so loosely attached to the inflorescence that they could be dispersed fairly easily, a necessity for self-perpetuation.

In an article in *Science* Mangelsdorf and his fellow workers have three very plausible theories for the lack of any present-day wild form of maize. One of these is that maize cultivation pre-empted the areas where wild maize could thrive. A second theory is that if there were still in existence any wild ancestors of maize after the white man arrived, the goat which came with him would soon have rendered the wild plant extinct by selective browsing. However, their third theory, which may sound strange at first, is the most probable. Maize, as it was improved for the use of man by breeding and selection, very soon assumed a form that could not perpetuate itself. The pollen from this improved corn, being wind-borne, could travel for miles, and if it pollinated wild maize plants, would make the resulting progeny incapable of perpetuating itself. In other words, cultivated maize could have bred the wild maize out of existence.

This, very briefly, is the story of the world's third most important food plant.

FOR FURTHER READING

"Corn Origins Clarified"; *Science News Letter*, Vol. 65, #10, p. 150; March 6, 1954.
Kempton, James, *"Maize, Our Heritage from the Indian"*; Annual Re-

port of the Board of Regents of the Smithsonian Institute, 1937 (pp. 358-408).

Mandelsdorf, P. C., "The Mystery of Corn," in *Plant Life;* Simon and Schuster, N.Y.C., 1957.

Mangelsdorf, P. C.; Richard S. MacNeish and Walton C. Galinat, *Domestication of Corn,* Science, Vol. 143, #3606, pp. 538ff, February, 1964.

Mangelsdorf, P. C. and R. G. Reeves, *Origin of Indian Corn and Its Relatives;* Texas Agricultural Experiment Station, Bulletin 574, 1939.

Walden, Howard T., *Native Inheritance: The Story of Corn in America;* Harper, 1966.

Wallace, Henry A. and W. L. Brown, *Corn and Its Early Fathers;* Michigan State University Press, 1956.

Weatherwax, Paul, *Indian Corn in Old America;* Macmillan Co., New York, 1954.

CHAPTER 7

The Stuff Called Pollen

S you may know, the stamens of flowering plants produce small structures called pollen grains. With few exceptions these must be transferred to the stigma of the same flower or, more often, another flower, prior to seed formation. The details of what happens following this transfer of pollen (called pollination) will be found in Chapter 19. Obviously the more efficient the process of pollen transfer, the more certain is the production of seed.

Pollen is spread from plant to plant by wind, by water, by insects (bees are very important here), and by birds. Many plants make very sure of seed formation by self-pollination, in which process the pollen-bearing anthers move to come into contact with the stigma of the same flower. Some plants employ both methods with part of their flowers arranged for cross-pollination and others for self-pollination. Fully self-pollinated flowers, because they do not need to attract bees, usually lack colorful petals. In some cases they are even formed under the surface of the soil.

There are many interesting stories connected with pollination. One concerns eel grass or tape grass, *Vallisneria americana*, sometimes known as wild or water celery which is common on the bottom of quiet, fresh waters along our eastern seaboard and inland west to the Dakotas. The female flowers, borne on very long, slender stems, open at the surface of the water. The male flowers are formed below the surface of the water. When the male flowers mature, they break free and float to the surface where each opens to expose three stamens. These male flowers are formed in enormous numbers and are blown about the surface of the water by the wind. A few of them are blown into contact with female flowers which are then pollinated. The pollinated female flowers close and, by a corkscrew-like twist of their stalks, are then withdrawn beneath the surface of the water where the seeds are formed.

The story of the yucca flower and the yucca moth is an intricate one. The female moth gathers a pellet of yucca pollen which she carries to an unfertilized[1] blossom. She climbs the style of the pistil and rams the pollen pellet into the funnel-like hollow of the stigma. Then she lays an egg on the ovary of the pistil and departs. As the seeds form, following fertilization, the egg containing the moth grub will hatch and the grub will eat a few of the seeds.

Much of the impetus for the study of pollen has come from the fact that some people are allergic to certain kinds of pollen in the air and develop "hay fever" and other unpleasant symptoms. It is difficult for a person who does not suffer from a pollen allergy to realize what torment an afflicted person may undergo. A bacteriologist of my acquaintance had trouble each late summer with a stuffed-up head and inflamed, running eyes. He had been born in the mountains of Greece where there was no hay fever. After several years of this he was told that ragweed was probably the cause of his trouble. Being a scientist, he tried an experiment to see if this were true. He went to a nearby vacant lot and found a sizable ragweed plant in full pollen-bearing condition. Cutting it carefully, he brought it back to the laboratory, went into a small closet, closed the door, and shook the plant. He told me later that he very nearly didn't come out of that closet alive. He could hardly breathe for some time. Doctors in testing pollen allergies place a small amount of suspected pollen in a scratch on the arm and watch for inflamation. Carefully done, this is a far safer test for allergy than that employed by my friend, the bacteriologist.

The first work on hay fever or seasonal asthma was started in England in 1873 by Charles Blackley. Today many scientists in the public health services are investigating pollen allergies. These workers sample the air for concentration of wind-borne pollens with specially designed pollen traps. Through long study experts are able to recognize the different kinds of pollen grains, which are usually quite characteristic in shape, size, markings, texture, and color. There have been cases of people showing allergic reaction to insect-borne pollen, for example, rose pollen; but only wind-borne pollen, as a general thing, becomes abundant enough in the air to cause much trouble.

---

[1]The terms "pollinate" and "fertilize," while not exactly synonymous, are used somewhat interchangeably. The word "pollinate" means to place the pollen on the stigma, while the word "fertilize" implies that a sexual fusion will have resulted from this process in the ovules, resulting in viable seeds. See Chapter 19 for details.

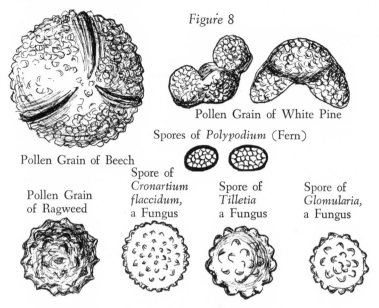

Figure 8

Pollen Grain of White Pine

Spores of *Polypodium* (Fern)

Pollen Grain of Beech

Pollen Grain
of Ragweed

Spore of
*Cronartium
flaccidum,*
a Fungus

Spore of
Tilletia
a Fungus

Spore of
Glomularia,
a Fungus

Pollen Grains, with Fern and Fungus Spores for Comparison

Wind-borne pollen is often formed in great quantities. If it were not, the changes of pollination and subsequent seed formation would be too low. In pine forests the surface of the soil, when pollen is being shed, sometimes appears to have been dusted with sulfur because of the heavy layer of pollen. Some of the wind-borne pollen will fall into streams or ponds. If these pollen grains are buried under organic debris or silt where there is insufficient oxygen to permit decay, the outer walls of the pollen grains may be preserved for millions of years. After proper treatment they may be examined under the microscope. Soft coals, bogs, and lake-bed deposits are particularly rich sources of fossil pollen grains (see Chapter 13). Of course, all such pollen is dead; in fact, most pollen, unless very carefully stored, is short lived. In nature the living content of most pollen grains is dead within a week or two following dissemination, and in many kinds of pollen it dies within twenty-four hours. The outer walls only have been preserved in fossil pollen.

Dr. G. Lagerheim (1860-1926), professor of botany at the University of Stockholm, was first to study fossil pollen. However, modern pollen analysis dates back only to 1916, when L. Von Post published a paper on the fossil pollen of Swedish bogs. Today a scientist skilled in the subject can take a soil sample from a stone hatchet or cooking utensil made by man thousands of years ago, examine it under a microscope, and reconstruct with considerable accuracy, if there are pollen grains in the adhering soil, the kinds of plants that grew in that region and from this the environment in which the aboriginal owner lived. In fact, considerable research is now in progress, to trace changes in climate, vegetation, and rates of erosion or sedimentation through past ages using fossil pollen grain counts as indicators of past conditions. For example, if we find considerable amounts of pollen of temperate zone conifers associated with a certain period and locality, we assume that the climate for that time and place would have been favorable for such trees.

However, the study of the pollen of bygone ages is not a simple one. Wind-borne pollen may be carried in the upper air currents for as much as a thousand miles. Pollen falling in streams may be deposited hundreds of miles from the plant that produced it. Pollen of insect-pollinated plants, because it is produced in relatively small amounts and because it is not commonly carried by wind, is much less frequently encountered. Pine, spruce, and certain other wind-borne pollen grains have walls comparatively resistant to decay, while the pollen of poplars and certain other plants decays rapidly except under conditions very favorable to its preservation. The spores of mosses, ferns, and fungi must be studied along with the pollen grains. They are often produced and deposited in large quantities. (Spores of fungi are, in many cases, very difficult to identify because the spore forms are often similar in widely different genera.) The student of fossil pollen must employ very sound judgment in his use of evidence from geological and archeological, as well as botanical sources, before forming his conclusions.

FOR FURTHER READING

Brown, G. F., *Pollen Slide Studies;* Charles C. Thomas, Springfield, Illinois, 1949.

Erdtman, D. G., *An Introduction to Pollen Grains,* Chronica Botanica; Waltham, Massachusetts, 1943. (This book handles the chemistry of manipulating pollen very well.)

Erdtman, D. G., *Pollen Morphology and Plant Taxonomy;* Hafner, (Revised), 1966.

Kapp, Ronald O., *How to Know the Pollen and Spores;* Brown, 1968.

Martin, Paul S., *Last 10,000 Years: A Fossil Pollen Record of the American Southwest;* University of Arizona Press, 1963.

Wodehouse, R. P., *Hay Fever Plants,* Chronica Botanica; 1945, Ronald Press, New York.

Wodehouse, R. P., *Pollen Grains, Their Structure, Identification and Significance in Science and Medicine;* McGraw-Hill Book Company, New York, 1935.

CHAPTER 8

So Many Marvels

TORIES of plants that ensnare and devour human beings and of plants so poisonous that their shadows can kill are mere fantasies. Such stories, however, are not much more incredible than the wonders that do exist in the world of plant life. Indeed, many common processes in plants (for example, photosynthesis) are miracles beyond our complete understanding.

We often think of plants as being stationary in contrast to the mobility of animals. Yet many plants move as though of their volition. Several of the microscopic algae, and the spores of other algae, propel themselves through water with whiplike structures or fringe-like appendages. These are not hard to find if one spends a little time examining stagnant water with a microscope. The male reproductive body of a fern will swim through even a droplet of water to reach and fertilize an "egg" held in a nearby flask-shaped structure. Such movements originate in the cell protoplasm — the living substance in the plants.

Several green plants can fold their leaves, some of them rather quickly. One such quick-folding plant is *Mimosa pudica,* related to peas and beans. At a touch the leaves fold together and the plant appears to wilt. It soon recovers. It is commonly called a sensitive plant. People often grow them as interesting house plants. Many other allied plants (clovers, for example) fold their leaves at night in "sleep movements."

Take note on a hot summer day how corn plants have their own specialized device for movement, the leaves rolling inward from the edges in dry weather to conserve moisture. This rolling of the leaves is accomplished through the action of large, bubble-like cells within the leaf tissue. These cells function by hydrostatic pressure. Rhododendrons and other evergreen plants use similar devices for conserving moisture in winter.

The Venus flytrap grasps and digests insects. The leaves are provided with three trigger hairs. When these are disturbed, the two halves of the leaf fold together, ensnaring the prey. Insects thus digested help to supply the plants with certain nutrients, among them nitrogen compounds. However, if a small pebble is used to trip the mechanism, it will be released. Gnats and other minute insects not worth eating are too small to affect the trap mechanism.

Figure 9

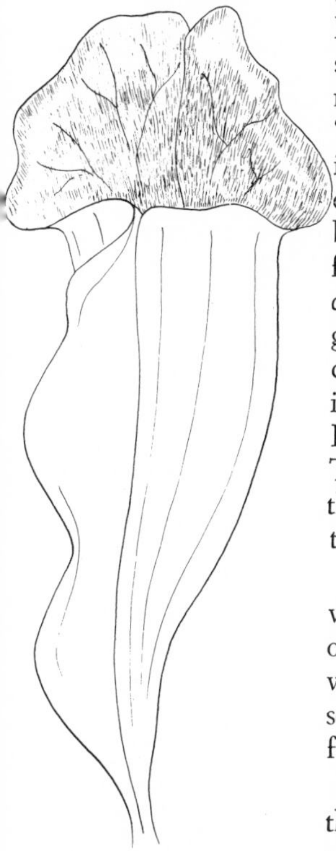

Pitcher plants are also insectivorous. However, they employ still a different principle. In some of them the entire leaf is pitcher-shaped, while in others the tip of the leaf is modified into a vase-shaped structure. These "pitchers" contain a liquid capable of digesting insects. In some pitcher plants the upper edge of the trap is provided with deflected bristles that prevent an insect, once caught, from escaping. Some (for example, *Sarracenia*) attract insects by means of nectar glands around the rim of the pitcher. The colored hoods of all of them are attractive to insects. *Darlingtonia* uses still another idea. It smells badly. This attracts carrion insects. These, when caught and drowned, add to the evil odor, and this, in turn, makes the trap even more attractive to carrion insects.

The leaves of the sundews are provided with sticky hairs. An insect alighting on one of these leaves is held by the sticky hairs, while other hairs fold over it and entrap it securely. The leaf then secretes digestive fluids to "devour" the victim.

Modified Leaves
of Pitcher Plants

Probably explainable, at least in part, on the basis of hydrostatic pressure, are the movements of many microscopic soil organisms that capture and devour the equally microscopic eel-worms or nematodes. This drama is going on in the soil all around us and under our very feet. There are quite a number of fungi that have learned this trick.

Many fungi and bacteria secrete antibiotics, such as penicillin. These antibiotics weaken or eliminate competition. It is probable that there are many antibiotics that are deadly to warm-blooded

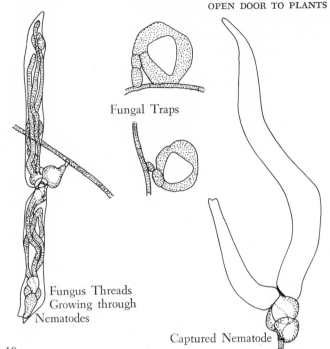

Fungal Traps

Fungus Threads
Growing through
Nematodes

Captured Nematode

Figure 10

Microscopic Fungi That Live on Microscopic Worms Called Nematodes

animals. One substance I worked with had antibiotic properties. It halted the growth of certain fungi while permitting one test fungus to grow. Further work showed that a pound of this, administered by injection under the belly skin, would kill eight and a half million white rats in less than an hour. It was also deadly when administered orally, but in a slightly larger dosage.

How do vines find supports on which to climb? Time-lapse photography shows that the unsupported vine terminals gyrate slowly but continuously until they encounter some fixed object. The tendrils (or in the absence of tendrils, the vine stems themselves) then twine around the support. Have you ever examined the direction of twining of a vine such as morning glory, climbing bean, or wild buckwheat? The bean plant always entwines in a counter-clockwise direction. It is an interesting experiment to untwine a bean plant and rewind it in a clockwise direction. It will promptly unwind itself and again resume its counter-clockwise spiral. Certain other vining species twine in a clockwise direction.

The designs of many extremely small plants are very beautiful. A microscope must be employed, however, to observe their beauty at first hand. The silica cases of the diatoms furnish an excellent example. These microscopic algae derive their name from the fact

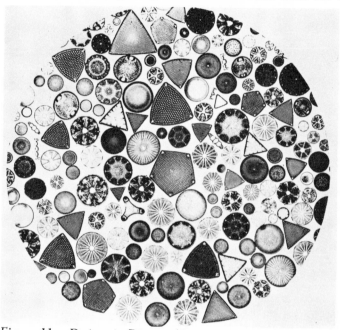

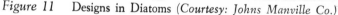

Figure 11   **Designs in Diatoms** (*Courtesy: Johns Manville Co.*)

that the cases consist of two halves which in many species look something like the two halves of a pill box ("diatom" means "cut through"). When the protoplasm within them dies, the shell-like silica cases, though nearly as fine as dust, may persist for millions of years, accumulating in vast numbers. Some deposits of diatomaceous earth are large enough to permit commercial exploitation. It is commonly used as a fine abrasive, insulating material and filler. Dynamite originally was made by absorbing nitroglycerine on diatomaceous earth.

Turning from microscopic forms to the opposite extreme, we find that the plant kingdom includes the largest organisms on earth. Just as there have never existed on this earth creatures larger than our largest whales, so there have never been, in all past geological history, plants more enormous than our present-day sequoias. There are eucalyptus trees in Australia that are even *taller*. One specimen is reported at 470 feet.. However, none of these giants has the *bulk* of the sequoia.

Here is a list of some of the largest trees:

Name of Tree	Location	Diameter	Height	Age
Western Yellow Pine	Western North America	8 ft.	230 ft.	500 yrs.
Sugar Pine	California	12 ft.	300 ft.	600 yrs.
Douglas Fir	British Columbia	25 ft.	417 ft.	700 yrs.
Redwood	California	28 ft.	360 ft.	1000 yrs.
Big Tree (Sequoia)	California	35 ft.	330 ft.	4000 yrs.
Big Cypress of Tule	Oaxaca, Mexico	50 ft.	140 ft.	5000 yrs.
Western Juniper	California	14 ft.	80 ft.	3000 yrs.
Norway Maple	Europe	6 ft.	80 ft.	500 yrs.
Sugar Maple	Wabash Valley	4 ft.	120 ft.	500 yrs.
Bur Oak	Wabash Valley	8 ft.	170 ft.	500 yrs.
Tulip	Wabash Valley	10 ft.	200 ft.	500 yrs.
Sycamore	Southern Indiana	16 ft.	150 ft.	500 yrs.
Black Walnut	Wabash Valley	6 ft.	150 ft.	500 yrs.

(From *Textbook of Botany* by Traneau, Sampson and Tiffany, courtesy Harper and Rowe.)

Banyan figs of Asia spread by dropping rootlike structures from the branches. When these reach the earth they become rooted and grow to form new trunks. One tree will continue to spread in this manner until it may shelter an entire village.

There are jack-in-the-pulpit relatives in some parts of the Asiatic tropics with the jack-in-the-pulpit part of the plant ten feet tall. One of the tree ferns, *Alsophila excelsa,* of Queensland grows to a height of sixty to eighty feet. A common tree fern in Hawaii has a trunk diameter of two feet. There are two different bamboo species that may reach a height of a hundred feet, and there are reports of some that are even taller. This is especially astonishing in that bamboos are grasses.

As for age, here again plants far outstrip the animal kingdom. The dragon tree of the Canary Islands may attain an age estimated by some authorities at six thousand years. Some of the bald cypresses of Mexico are around four thousand years old, and so are some of the bristle-cone pines of our West Coast. Recently a colony of box huckleberry in Perry County, Pennsylvania, has been under examination — it is believed that this plant may be thirteen thousand years old. If this is true, it would be the oldest of all living plants that have been studied to date.

Most seeds under natural conditions are fairly short-lived, although it is known that mustard seed (*Brassica* spp.) and buttonweed seed (*Abutilon Theophrasti*) will lie dormant and viable in undisturbed

Figure 12

The Multiple Stems of *Bourreria cumanensis* (Guatacaro Tree)

soil for fifty years. Recently lotus seeds, dated through radio-active carbon and found to be three thousand years old, were excavated from deposits below Tokyo, Japan. These were shown to be still capable of germination. (Dating by means of radioactive carbon is now standard practice.)[1]

Often our ideas on how and where plants may grow may come in for a rude revision. We are accustomed to think of cactus plants as dwellers of hot, arid deserts. However, some species of cactus grow in Iowa, the Dakotas and even up into Canada where winter temperatures may drop in minus forty degrees Fahrenheit. Certain cactus species, for example *Rhipsalis* spp., grow in relatively moist areas. *Pereskia* grows as a tree with normal leaves. Except for its spines and the form of its flowers, you might not recognize it as a cactus. Plants grow how and where they can. Through natural selection, over long periods of time, they often become greatly modified and specialized, the better to fit into their environments. We are surrounded by herbaceous and woody plants that grow in a manner with which we are familiar. When we travel in new regions we become more and more willing to admit that if a plant (or animal) can feed itself and reproduce, nothing more is necessary for its continued existence. Its structure is merely functional, contributing to those two all-important processes. For example, we are used to seeing trees with reasonably cylindrical trunks. But the guatacaro (*Bourreria*), a small tree of northern South America, can't seem to decide whether to have several separate trunks or a single trunk made up of several individual trunks fused together. It is possible to find all gradations, from distinctly separate trunks to reasonably cylindrical single trunks. Fluted trunks occur in the unrelated *Alseis trichocarpa* of northern South America. In Alseis, however, there is no apparent effect of a fusion of trunks. The unrelated *Aspidosperma* of South America also has a fluted trunk.

In Figure 12 you can see in the middle background a tree trunk that is mottled white on dark, much like our sycamore tree. This is palo Maria (Mary's tree), related to rhubarb. It will be referred to later in this chapter. You can see also, in the upper left hand corner of the photograph, vines that grow in a zigzag manner. This manner of growth permits them to lengthen without breaking when the wind sways the trees. This picture was taken during the dry season in the jungles about 150 miles east of Caracas, Venezuela,

---

[1]The techniques of radioactive carbon dating are described in *National Geographic*, August, 1958, p. 234.

Figure 13

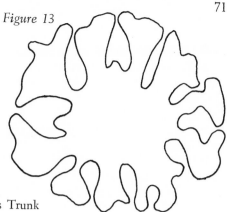

Cross Section of Alseis Trunk

where jaguars are fairly common and howler monkeys roar practically continuously.

Some plants grow in shapes that can only be described as weird.
Pachypodium of South Africa is found growing in arid places,
and the plants look like huge inverted carrots. Probably the oddest

Figure 14

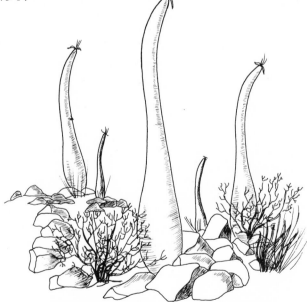

Pachypodium namaquanum of South Africa

of all plants from the standpoint of structure is *Welwitschia,* found in the desert regions of South Africa. The plant consists of a great cuplike (or saddlelike) structure about two feet across with straplike leaves attached to the edges of the underground stem. There are only two of these, and as you can see from Figure 15, they be-

Figure 15

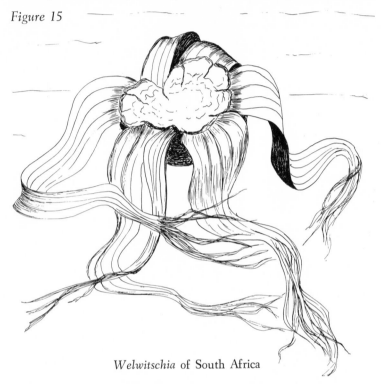

Welwitschia of South Africa

come frayed by the desert winds. To me they suggest an octopus spreading out over the sand.[2]

Manner of growth is closely related to function. Cactuses with accordion-pleated stems or with the stem segments flat and bellows-like can expand rapidly and easily as they take in water following occasional desert showers. These devices are so successful that they are employed by totally unrelated plants. For example, there are desert plants in the milkweed family and in the euphorbia family that have accordion pleats so closely resembling those found in cer-

[2]At this writing the Montreal Botanical Garden in Montreal, Canada, has growing and on display nine plants of Welwitschia, three of which are over twenty years old. One of the older plants has flowered several times.

tain cacti that the untrained observer would certainly call them cacti.

Devices employed by plants in self-defense are enormous in number. In Chapter 4 we discussed the use of chemicals by some of them to discourage competition. Thorns, briars, prickles, and stinging hairs are widely distributed through the plant kingdom, and have obviously evolved independently many times because they are found in unrelated families. A glance at any weedy pasture is sufficient to show that many plants escape being eaten simply because they contain chemicals unpalatable to grazing animals.

An odd means of defense in which the plant takes no action is the presence of ants. By one estimate, nearly three thousand species of plants are protected by diverse species of ants, as many people have discovered to their sorrow. I remember the rude shock I got in Venezuela when I first gathered some of the lovely yellow flowers of carnesto lendas (*Cochlospermum vitifolium*). The ants that covered them had jaws like tigers. The palo Maria (*Triplaris* spp.)[3], a South-American tree as tall and straight as a pine, and related to rhubarb, (and unrelated *Cecropia* spp.) harbors ants that hollow out the pith through the whole plant and live in these galleries. I once sent two obreros[4] to cut a palo Maria for a ridge pole while putting up a field house in Venezuela. When they returned, I asked if there were many ants. "Si, bastante!" (Yes, plenty!), was the reply — with very broad grins. When you cut these trees you whack at the trunk with your axe, step back, brush the ants off yourself, and whack again. You are well bitten by the time the tree is down. Many trees have hollow thorns that afford a dwelling place for ants. I have encountered this in *Fagara monophylla,* an orange relative, and in several of the acacias (Leguminosae) in South America. Many such acacias secrete sugar and albumen which are eaten by the ants, who in turn may repel harmful insects from the plant. In the United States you may observe ants swarming over unopened peony flower buds. Watch for this in the late spring or early summer. (The same thing may be observed on many kinds of trees as they come into leaf. The ants are gathering a sugary substance that occurs on the buds.)

We could continue our list of wonders almost without end, but

---

[3]sp. indicates a species, not specified, while spp. indicates that several species are concerned.

[4]The word "obrero," much used in South America, means worker or helper.

with this much of an introduction, let's close on a happy note —
a picture of the seed capsules of the ordinary snapdragon.

Figure 16

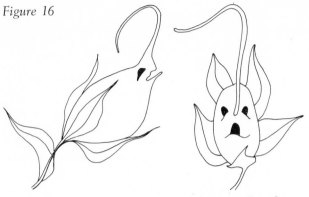

Seed Capsules of Common Snapdragon

CHAPTER 9

Fruits of the World*

F it were not for the rose family, the dwellers of the temperate zone would be in a poor way for native fruits. In this one family belong apple, pear, quince (both common and Chinese), juneberry, the many plums and cherries, strawberries, raspberries, blackberries, dewberries, peach, and apricot. Plant relationships are traced through the flowers, and all of these members of the family Rosaceae have five sepals, five petals and many stamens. The number of pistils will vary. Their number is related to the form the fruit will finally take. Thus, plums, cherries, peach, and apricot, with a single seed, have flowers with single pistils; while aggregate fruits like raspberry, blackberry and dewberry have many. The close relationship between pear and apple is obvious to any observant person. Each fruit has five compartments for seeds, and so the pistil is five-pointed.

Rubus, the genus for raspberries and the like, and *Prunus,* the genus in which we find cherries, plums, peach, and apricot, have members distributed through the temperate regions of much of the world. There are scores of different species, and the fruits of most of them are at least edible, if not delicious.

A few more plant families supply fruits in the temperate zone. From the heather family (Ericaceae) we obtain the many blueberries, whortelberries, and huckleberries. All of these are in the genus *Vaccinium.* Members of the genus are found in many parts of the world, and the fruits of most species are edible. However, one species in the mountain of Central America is reported to bear poisonous fruits, so it might be well to ask before eating if you encounter *Vaccinium* species in your travels. The cranberry belongs here too; it is placed in *Vaccinium* by some authorities, and

---

*Many of the illustrations for this chapter were adapted, with permission, from the Chicago National History Museum's publication "Tropical and Subtropical Fruits" by B. E. Dahlgren, illustrated by Albert Frey.

Oxycoccus by others. Try the fruits of the wintergreen plant sometime; there is not much to them, but they do have a pleasant wintergreen flavor. This family, by the way, is very large and widely distributed. Azaleas, rhododendrons, and many other ornamental shrubs
belong here.

Currants and gooseberries are in genus *Ribes*. There are several
flowering shrubs that are related, but which do not bear fruits.
Other than flowering currant, there are such familiar names as
Hydrangea, Astilbe and mock orange (*Philadelphus*). The family is
the Saxifragaceae.

Bush currants should not be confused with the packaged dried
currants you buy at the grocery store. The latter are obtained from
a species of grape, as are raisins. All grapes are in the single genus
Vitis, family Vitaceae. There are dozens of species distributed over
the world, many of which bear very good fruits. The name currant,
by the way, is derived from Corinth in Greece.

All of our melons are members of the gourd family (Cucurbitaceae), along with squash and pumpkin. Both watermelon and muskmelon are grown in great variety in the temperate zones, as well
as in the tropics. The muskmelons grown in our area are mostly
the netted or nutmeg type — scientifically *Cucumis melo* variety
reticulata. The name cantaloupe, so often applied to them, belongs
more properly to *Cucumis melo* variety *cantaloupensis,* more commonly grown in the old world. The true cantaloupe has a hard,
warty or scaly rind which is more or less furrowed. The flesh of this
form varies in color through red, white, green, and yellow. However,
like many other names that have been improperly applied, it is
probable that we will continue to call our netted melons cantaloupes.
The Persian melon is merely a variety of the netted melon. A few
of the large, yellow cassaba melons also appear in the markets.
Further south the curuba or cassabanana is grown. The fruits are
as much as two feet long — and slender. They are heavily scented.
These are in a different genus than muskmelons and are classified
as *Sicana odorifera.* However, there is also an elongated relative of
our common melon, the *Cucumis melo* variety *flexuosus.* This is
called the snake or serpent melon. It grows to three feet in length
and is often coiled. It is grown for a curiosity and for preserves. The
preserves, as you would imagine, are rather intensely flavored.
Cucumis melo variety *dudaim,* the dudaim melon, with fruits the
size of an orange, is so heavily scented that it is used in perfumery.

In these five families we have listed all the fruits of any great
importance grown in temperate North America. However, many of

the better fruits grown in the northern United States are very worthy competitors in quality to those grown in any part of the world. Quantities of apples, pears, plums, and grapes are imported into South America from the United States. On the other hand, we are able to procure on the market many of the more desirable tropical or subtropical fruits.

Certain other plant families are the source of a large number of fruits; Rutaceae[1] is one of these. From this family we obtain orange, lemon, grapefruit, tangerine, lime, and kumquat. There are several less familiar citrus relatives. The enormous shaddock which was supposed to have been brought from the Old World to the Barbadoes by Captain Shaddock in 1696, is pear-shaped with coarse, rather dry flesh and is not very desirable. However, it is probably one parent of the grapefruit, which originated in comparatively recent times, apparently as a chance cross with some other citrus species, somewhere in the West Indies. The preserved citron of commerce is made from the thick peel of the large-fruited *Citrus medica*. This fruit has been in cultivation for centuries in the Mediterranan region. It should not be confused with the watermelon relative called a citron. The two are not at all related.

The calamondin is a very attractive fruit in this group. It is rather small, brilliant orange-red and very tart. It is used for beverages and for marmalade.

Commercial orange marmalade is not made from the familiar sweet orange, but from another species, the sour orange. Sour orange is much used in the United States and other parts of the world as root stocks for other citrus species. This is done because in heavy, wet soils a disease called "footrot" causes trouble if sweet orange is the root stock. Sour orange shows considerable resistance to the disease. However, sour orange root stocks are killed if the plant becomes infected with tristeza virus. Sweet orange root stocks are more tolerant to the virus, and where the virus is a problem, sweet orange makes the better root stocks. In either case, the seeds are planted and the desired citrus species grafted onto the root part of the young seedling.

There are, in addition to the many citrus fruits we have listed, quite a number of citrus hybrids, such as the very delicious tangelo varieties, the limequat and citrange. If you have never tasted a

---

[1]The name is taken from *Ruta graveolens,* the rue of the old-fashioned garden.

tangelo, do so at your earliest opportunity. If well ripened, it is delicious.

There is a New World relative of citrus which bears edible fruits, the white sapote. It is native to Central America and is grown to some extent in Florida. The fruits are rather small and resemble somewhat a green tomato in appearance. There are several very acceptable varieties.

When we buy bananas in the States we almost always buy the variety known as Gros Michel which would be "Big Mike" in English. The Venezuelans call it Cuyaco. Big Mike is a good name for it. The plants are often twenty feet tall, and the bunches can be enormous. Another Latin American name for the variety is quiniento which means "five hundred" referring to the number of fruits per bunch. In the tropics, however, the number of varieties of bananas and plantains is enormous, varying from the little finger bananas — varities which you can eat like popcorn — to the enormous horse plantains, often a foot long. The plantains (platanos in South America) are the cooking bananas. (The natives often cook and eat the flower buds of the banana plants as well.) Bananas we buy are picked in what is called the fit stage, which means that they are still pretty green. In the tropics they can be left until the full stage. Gathered then they are a far more delicious fruit. They are always gathered before they are fully ripened, probably because parrots, monkeys, and other creatures would rip them to pieces in a hurry if they were left to ripen on the plant.

The cultivated banana varieties and the plantains are all derived from *Musa paradisiaca* which probably was native to India. These are now cultivated in all parts of the world where climatic conditions will permit. They are extremely important in the food economy of many tropical countries. In much of South America, for example, bananas and the related plantains, along with corn, black beans, rice and yuca (the source of tapioca) make up most of the diet of the common people.

The sweet banana varieties are occasionally classified as *Musa sapientum,* and by other authorities as *Musa paradisiaca* variety *sapientum.* "Sapientum" would indicate that it is the fruit of wise men. (Could this mean that by the time a man becomes wise his teeth have become unfit for any fruit firmer than bananas?) There are several other *Musa* species, some with edible fruits, with or without seeds, depending on species, and some, like Manila hemp, the fruits of which are not edible.

There is a tremendous variation among the many pineapple

varieties. In size they vary from delicious little "individual pines" to very large varieties such as the Cabezona which may bear fruits weighing fifteen pounds or more. The pineapple we know has a single spire of leaves at the top. There are varieties that have a cluster of such leaf spires. Shapes also vary from much elongated to nearly spherical.

Pineapples that arrive fresh on the northern markets are a very sorry substitute for fresh, fully ripened pineapples eaten where they are grown. Many of the very choicest varieties won't stand shipment, and even those that are harvested for shipping are picked grass green.

The pineapple is one of the many gifts of the South American Indians to the world's foods. Like maize, the beginnings of its culture are lost in the mists of antiquity. Unlike maize, however, its inedible wild ancestor is known. It grows to this day in South American jungles. There are a few related species with edible fruits.

Pineapple has a firm place in tribal symbolism, being associated with hospitality. It is not hard to see how this might have come about. I recall the day I arrived with my family at a very modern hotel in Barquisimeto, in Venezuela. We had driven for many miles in a jeep across the dusty desert and were in a sorry condition when we arrived. Scarcely had we finished our very welcome showers when the assistant manager of the hotel came to our door with a huge tray of sliced, chilled pineapple fresh from the fields that stretch all around the city. What a way to welcome guests! It was as juicy as watermelon. In the past, conventionalized pineapple decorations were often carved on the tops of bedposts in the United States. These decorations may have been suggested by the hospitality concept.

As for the avocado, it is true that we of the northern United States have become accustomed to varieties grown in California or Florida; but this fruit (which is related to cinnamon, sassafras, and camphor) has been cultivated for centuries by Central American Indians. In many parts of South America avocados are important in the native diet. They are rich in both protein and oil and are so nutritious as to form a fair substitute for meat. Well-ripened avocado is also tasty in soups.

We have seen that many fruits are members of large families. The pomegranate is one of only two species of the family *Punicaceae*. However, there are numerous varieties of pomegranate. The pomegranate is a bush with attractive red flowers. Along with grapes, figs, and olives, pomegranate is one of the fruits mentioned in the Bible as a part of the good things the Hebrews were to find in the promised land (Deut. 8:8). The conventionalized pomegranate fruit was used in the decorations on the priestly robes (Exodus 28:33; 39:24) and on the pillars of the temple (I Kings 7:18; II Kings 25:17; II Chron. 3:16). It is said that King Solomon had an orchard of pomegranates.

Dates are not specifically mentioned in the Bible, which at first glance seems odd because it is well known that the date has long been cultivated in Bible lands. But the date is in the Bible, nevertheless, just a bit concealed. Whenever a girl named Tamar is mentioned (Gen. 36:6; II Sam. 13:1; 14:27), the date is implied, because this name means "date palm." Almost certainly the phrase in Psalm 92:12, ". . . the righteous shall flourish like the palm," refers to the date palm. Jericho is often referred to as the City of Palms, while Bethany, mentioned many times in the Bible, is probably best translated "House of Unripe Dates." It was near the Mount of Olives. The cultivated date has been an important part of the diet of the Old World tropics from early times. Records of it are abundant in the writings of the ancient Egyptians and Assyrians, for instance.

The cultivated dates we know are varieties of *Phoenix dactylifera*. Although it is not certain where the species originated, it was very probably North Africa or western Asia. There are a few other species with edible fruits, for example the Ceylon date (*Phoenix zeylanica*) and the *Phoenix acaulis* of India; and there are quite a number of species whose fruits are not edible.

Many edible fruits have poisonous relatives. The Kaffir orange of Africa is the fruit of *Strychnos spinosa*, a relative of the poisonous strychnine species. As its common name indicates, it is about the size and shape of an orange, but it has a rather hard shell. The contents are soft, juicy, and pleasant to eat, having a spicy flavor. However, we don't have to go to the tropics to pick fruits from poisonous plants. The leaves of several of the wild cherries contain enough prussic acid (Hydrogen cyanide) to make them a very real menace to livestock. The fruits of the may-apple are edible, but the root is poisonous. May-apple is quite common in our northern woods.

Several edible fruits occur in that rather poisonous family the Sapindaceae. Buckeye and horse-chesnut are related, both of them inedible. The akee (*Blighia sapida*), native to West Africa, but widely planted, is a relative with edible fruits. It was named after Captain Bligh of "Mutiny on the Bounty" ill-fame. The fruit is poisonous before it is ripe, but when ripe the pulp is edible and delicious. However, it is reported that once it has become overripe it is again poisonous. Another member of the family, *Melicocca bijuga* of South America, is consumed in great quantities. The common names include mamon, mamoncillo, genip, and Spanish-lime. The fruits are spherical, about an inch in diameter, with a brittle, green rind and a large stone. The pulp is a bit slimy, but has a very agreeable acid flavor. When I was in Venezuela I would frequently see an official on the other side of the grating in some office contentedly working on a mamon while he tended to my business. "Working on" is written advisedly. Once the rind is removed, the pulp clings to the stone, and the consumer works the thing over until he reaches what an economist would term "the point of diminishing returns" before he gives up and starts in on the next one. I recall that our South American laundress dribbled mamon juice on one of my wife's best white blouses while she was ironing it. The juice stains badly and permanently. Both akee and mamon can be grown in southern Florida.

Also in the Sapindaceae are the several *Nephelium* species native to Asia. The lychee is the best known of these. The fruits, which have a single large stone like the mamon, are about one and a half inches long, not quite that thick, and are encased in a thin, warty, globular "shell," bright scarlet in color. When fresh, the pulp is white, juicy, and very tasty. When dried the pulp becomes raisin-like. The Chinese consider the lychee their best fruit, superior to orange and peach.

Almost as unexpected as edible fruits from strychnine relatives are several from members of the Euphorbiaceae, the spurge, poinsettia, and castor bean family. The number of poisonous plants in this family is legion. Many of them are sources of arrow poisons (see chapter on poisonous plants). Among the edible fruits in this family we should mention Otaheite gooseberry which is native to Madagascar and tropical Asia, but naturalized in southern Florida and the West Indies. The rather small tree bears three-lobed fruits about the size, tartness, and color of green gooseberries. They make very acceptable pies.

Still another family notorious for poisonous plants, the Apocynaceae or dogbane family, contributes to our list. Of the many species of *Carissa* bearing edible fruits, Natal plum is the best known. The fruits are dark purple red, more or less plum-shaped, one to two inches long, many-seeded and have a raspberry-like flavor. Many plants in this family secrete latex. The *Carissa* fruits, when you bite into them, will bleed latex which is rather startling. The plants are attractive, thorny bushes and are much used for hedges in tropical and subtripical locations. They are fairly common in Florida.

But now for the climax. Our old friend poison ivy (which isn't an ivy) with its relatives poison oak (which isn't an oak) and poison sumac (it is a sumac — shoemake, really, because sumac leaves have long been used for tanning leather) are all in the Anacardiaceae, which is a particularly fruitful family. The most important of these fruits is the mango, native to tropic Asia but widely distributed.

Figure 17

The Mango

Mangos vary in size from less than two inches long to well over five, depending on variety. The shape is that of a somewhat flattened plum. The range of varieties is enormous. Some of the better cultivated forms are excellent, if you like mango. The flesh is yellow and very rich — too rich for some palates. Some of the poorer varieties have a turpentinelike flavor. The fruit and foliage of several wild species of mango produce skin blistering practically identical with that caused by poison ivy. For that matter, some people get a poison-ivy sort of blistering from the skins of ordinary mangos. It is probable that all of the poisonous principle is in the peel.

Mango trees grow to a very large size. A harvest of twenty to thirty bushels per tree in a season is not unusual. With the more common varieties in the tropics no attempt is made, as a rule, to pick the fruits higher on the tree. They just drop — and when they drop from a height of forty feet they hit the ground, or bystanders, with a mighty thump. During the mango season, which is at its height for three months, the natives do their best to eat all the mangos, but it is an impossible task. I have seen bushels of them rotting on the ground.

The cashew, also in the poison ivy family, is native to the New World. The nut, which is botanically the fruit, is attached to an enlarged, fleshy flower stalk called the merey. The merey is yellow

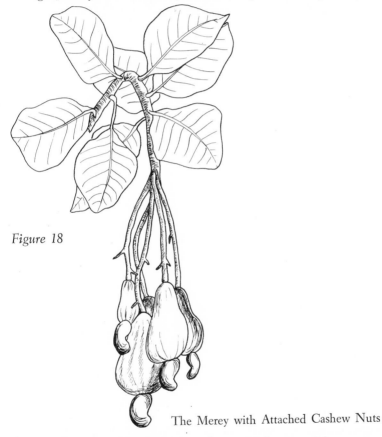

Figure 18

The Merey with Attached Cashew Nuts

or red when ripe. It is fragrant and very good to eat either raw or cooked. The rind of the nut, however, contains oils similar to those in poison ivy. These oils are expelled on roasting, but care is taken to avoid contact with the blistering fumes as the oils are driven off. Recently somebody in Haiti conceived the bright idea of decorating the tops of swizzle sticks (used in stirring mixed drinks) with unroasted cashew nuts. Several people received a poison-ivylike blistering from them.

There are a number of other more or less edible fruits related to poison ivy. Certainly for a family with such an unsavory reputation, these fruits constitute a strong bid for respectability. We should mention in passing that the pistachio nut, widely cultivated in the Mediterranean region, is another relative.

The sea-grape is an unusual fruit. It is in the family Polygonaceae in which we also find buckwheat, smartweed, sour dock and rhubarb. These fruits are borne on a shrub or tree that usually grows near the beach all through the Caribbean region. The South Americans call it *uva de la playa,* literally, beach grape. The fruits are in clusters like grapes and when ripe, have a pleasant, tart flavor. When the trees grow very near the acean, the fruits have a somewhat salty taste which is lacking in fruits growing farther inland. Sea grapes make very good jelly. The tree is usually less than twenty feet high, but it can become rather thick — I have seen eighteen-inch trunks. In South America the wood of these trees is blackish red, compact, just a little softer than granite and takes a satiny finish. Trees that I have cut in Florida have pinkish wood, but it is about as hard as that grown on the other side of the Caribbean.

Jack-in-the-pulpit relatives, in the family Araceae, often contain microscopic, needlelike, calcium oxalate crystals. Woodsmen who know this sometimes inveigle a greenhorn into tasting a bit of jack-in-the-pulpit bulb just to see their victim squirm when his tongue is tortured by the microscopic needles. It may astonish you that the "jack" of one of the Araceae is a fruit. This is the ceriman, also called *pinanona* by South Americans because of the resemblance to a pineapple and to fruits in the Anonnaceae. Ceriman is native to Mexico but is grown in the warmer parts of the United States and is very common in tropical displays in greenhouses (or even grown as a house plant) where its large decorative leaves never fail to attract attention. The fruit is very fragrant, with a flavor resembling a combination of pineapple and banana. The flesh is rather soft and very sweet. It contains a few calcium oxalate crystals which, however, are very few in fully-ripened fruits. The ceriman is quite commonly sold in fancy fruit stores in New York City, unfortunately at a fancy price.

Do you know *Oxalis,* with leaves resembling clover and with pink or yellow flowers? When we were children, this was one of the common "sour grassses" on which we used to browse. Native to tropic

Figure 19

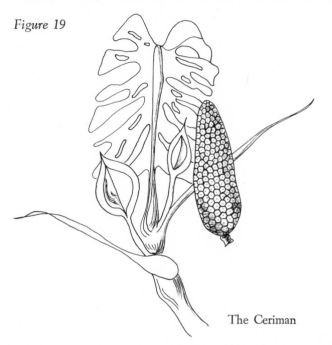

The Ceriman

Asia are two commonly cultivated trees, the bilimbi and the carambola, that are related to oxalis. The bilimbi is known only in cultivation. It is, therefore, a cultigen. Cultigens are plants that have been grown by man for so many centuries that no wild forms can be placed in the same species. The bilimbi is the larger tree, attaining a height of fifty feet; the carombola is usually about half as tall. If you have ever seen the seed pods of *Oxalis* and can imagine them enlarged to four or five inches in ength and correspondingly thickened, you will have a fair mental picture of these fruits. The carambola is distinctly star shaped in cross section, while the bilimbi is obscurely five-angled and looks vaguely like a cucumber. As might be expected from the family name which is derived from a word meaning acid, the fruits are very sour, but they may be eaten either raw or cooked. Bilimbi fruits are clustered along the trunk of the tree on which they grow. The carambola fruits are more conventional, however, and are borne on the branches.

The enormous family, the Passifloraceae, furnishes the many edible passion fruits. The very elaborate flowers of this family, with their three-pointed pistils, have somehow become mixed up in the symbolism of the Christian religion. Possibly they suggest the holy trinity. Hence, the word "passion" applies in the same sense that it does in the passion play. The largest of these fruits is the giant yellow-green granadilla or parcha (*Passiflora guadrangulans*) about the size of a cantaloupe. The pulp is eaten, seeds and all. The seeds are crunchy, like grapenuts. Passion fruits grow on vines, and their juice is often used for beverage. A relative, the may-pop (*Passiflora incarnata*), with edible fruits grows in the eastern United States, although most passion fruits are tropical.

A large portion of the cactus fruits are more or less edible, and some of them are delicious. Others, as one of my friends once remarked, taste like discouraged watermelons. The names pitajalla and pitajaya (both pronounced pē-tă-hă-yā), are applied rather indiscriminately to many species. *Opuntia* species are called prickly pears, or tunas, although the word tuna should probably be applied more particularly to the fruits of *Opuntia tuna,* with red berries an inch in length. In Venezuela all of them appear to be called tunas. The saguaro (or sahuaro) is the fruit of a plant familiar to the northerner, through photographs, at least, as the giant cactus of the Southwest. Fruits of this cactus are quite large, up to three inches in length, and are eaten raw, candied, made into preserves or jellies, or dried. The Indians make a syrup of them.

One wouldn't ordinarily think of bean relatives as fruit trees, but the pods of several species contain a very edible pulp. That of the tamarind, although it contains much sugar, is very acid and is best used for beverages. In South America there are several species of *Inga* with pods lined with white, very flavorful pulp. Frequently, while eating them, one must be content to eat the part of the pulp the worms haven't yet gotten around to. A very appropriate English name is ice-cream bean. In much of South America they are called guamos.

It is not generally known that the cacao seeds, from which we obtain cocoa and chocolate, may be eaten raw, and that they are very tasty. The pulp surrounding the seeds is also edible and a Brazilian has learned how to make excellent jelly of this pulp. However, he is keeping his method a secret. A cacao tree looks like a small beech tree with acorn squashes (of many colors, though only one maturity color to each tree) sprouting anywhere on the tree, even near the base of the trunk. The related *Cola acuminata* of Africa is the source of cola nut, used in flavoring the several popular cola beverages.

The common jujube, a member of the buckthorn or cascara family, is a native of China and has been cultivated there for ages. The fruits vary in quality and range in size from one to two inches in diameter. The shape is also variable from plum-shaped to almost

Figure 20

The Jujube

pear-shaped. The flavor varies from sweet to slightly sour. They may be eaten raw, dried, candied, or preserved. The fruits are dark brown when ripe, with crisp white flesh. It is important to grow only the better varieties. In reasonably protected locations, they can be grown as far north as New York City. There are many other fruits in this family.

While I wrote the first draft of this chapter in Venezuela, I took a few minutes to go to a nearby fruit store. They had some very fine anons[2] for sale, and I brought several of them home and munched on one of them from time to time as I wrote. Anons are somewhat heart-shaped, juicy, sub-acid, and very tasty. The family for this fruit, the Annonaceae, is one I hope you become familiar with someday, as there are several excellent fruits in the group. The related pawpaw of the southern United States looks like a small lumpy banana and has a very intense flavor. It is not by any means the best of these fruits. Doubtless that honor would go to the cherimoya. Guanabana or soursop can be eaten fresh, but the

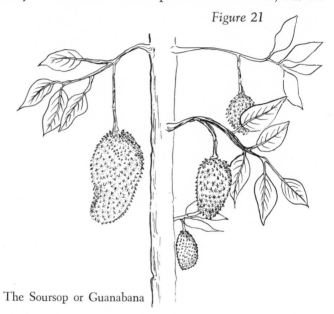

Figure 21

The Soursop or Guanabana

flavor is rather strong. It is excellent in ice cream. The manirote of South America is rather too intense in flavor for the average palate.

All of the several fruits in this family are composed of segments, more or less fused, giving some of them an appearance vaguely suggestive of pineapple. In some of them, for example the pond apple, the fusion of parts is so complete that only traces of the separate segments can be seen.

Do you live where the persimmons grow? Look at the persimmon tree with respect, for it is a member of the ebony family, the

[2]Other names for the anon include custard apple, sweet sop, and bullock's heart.

Ebenaceae, and even belongs to the same genus as do practically all of the ebonies. There are many species, widely distributed, that furnish the black heartwood known as ebony, in commercial quantities, though our native persimmon does not. The scientific name of the genus, *Diospyros,* means "pear of the gods." The fruits of our native persimmon you may not find very tasty (although I like them), but the big, red-orange Japanese persimmon, native to Japan and China, is a delicious fruit. It is grown rather commonly in Florida and California and is frequently on sale in the northern markets. Native to Mexico is the related black sapote, a dark brown fruit with chocolate-colored flesh. It is spicy in flavor and a bit too sweet. It is usually eaten with lemon or lime juice. A list of all the edible species of persimmon would indeed be long, and there are many more that are not edible.

The coconut from the botanical as well as the practical point of view, is a fruit. The trees usually are near the sea, and it has been assumed that the fruits are adapted to dispersal by ocean currents. This is emphatically denied by Thor Heyerdahl, author of the book *Kon Tiki.* He is convinced that the nut would not survive a long period of floating on salt water. This member of the palm family is so widespread that no botanist can say with certainty where it originated. Some say Asia or the East Indies. Heyerdahl believes it originated in the New World.

The importance of coconuts in the native economy and in world commerce is enormous. World market reports estimate the annual commercial crop somewhere near ten billion nuts. They constitute one of the most important sources of vegetable oil. The land to produce all these nuts would include an area of about ten thousand square miles. If this were one field, that field would be a hundred miles square. One of my friends with experience in the Philippines contends that these figures are too low; he claims there is a single field on Luzon that is almost fifty miles square.

Native to tropical America is the peach palm or pejibaye (pronounced pā-hē-bă-yă). This very thorny palm bears clusters of plumlike or peachlike fruits ranging in color from yellow to scarlet or red-brown. In certain cultivated varieties they may attain a diameter of two inches, and the clusters a weight of fifty pounds. The flesh is mealy, starchy, and highly nutritious. It is usually eaten cooked. The boiled fruits have a delicious, nutlike flavor.

The family Sapotaceae is represented by several very edible fruits in the tropics (and some which you may not approve of). The nispero or sapodilla fruit is about as large as a small orange, rough, dark brown outside, and has very sweet, juicy, well-flavored flesh. It is one of the definitely better fruits. The tree is the source of chicle, used for chewing gum. The related mammee sapote is widely cultivated in the tropics. The more or less spherical fruits are borne on a tree that may grow to a height of one hundred feet. The fruits are russetted, with firm flesh varying from pink to red-brown; they sometimes reach a diameter of eight inches. If your taste runs to tangy fruits, the flavor of the mammee sapote may be rather cloying, but a great many people like them.

In spite of a similarity of names, the mammee sapote is not related to mamey or mamey apple, which is in the family Guttiferae. The mamey grows in tropic America and is also russet. It is a bit flattened like a tomato and often weighs two pounds or more. It has a golden yellow flesh that tastes like very rich peaches. Mangosteen, in the same family, is native to the East Indies. The four to six seeds of the mangosteen are imbedded in the snow-white pulp, the extremely edible part. The pulp and seeds are enclosed in a thick, astringent rind. The fruit is about the size and shape of an orange, but is dark purplish or dark red. This is one of the very finest fruits.

Figure 22

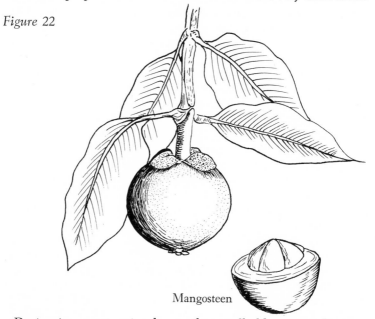

Mangosteen

Durian is a great, spiny horror that smells like a cross between Limburger cheese and garlic. If you eat it, you will develop a breath like a buzzard's. Yet this vile fruit is considered a great delicacy in tropical Asia. Monkeys and even tigers enjoy them. Durian is in the family Bombacaeae.[3] It is native to Malaya. However, it is widely distributed in the Asiatic tropics. The fruits weigh from five to ten pounds, and falling durian fruits are dangerous. People have been killed by them. The flesh is rich, sweet, and delicious, fresh or dried, once you get it past your nose. Anyone who likes strong cheeses can quickly develop a taste for them. If you eat them, however, be sure your friends are also partaking if you wish to remain socially acceptable. Seriously, the durian is one of the most highly prized fruits of the Orient. Incidentally, it is very nutritious. (There are several other more or less edible durian species.) The fuzzy fruits of the related monkey-bread of Africa may attain the length of a foot. The trees on which these two fruits are borne, like many of the other trees in the Bombacaceae, may grow to enormous sizes, even to thirty-foot diameters. In South America we find the related castaño, with football-sized brown fruits filled with chestnutlike seeds. When cooked, these starchy seeds are edible and much resemble a chesnut in flavor. *Castaño* means chestnut in Spanish.

Papaya, although native to South America, is such a desirable fruit that it is widely grown. The appearance of a papaya plant (it is not a true tree because it isn't woody) is outlandish. Imagine that you hang a great many fruits, ranging from the size of an acorn squash to a fair-sized watermelon, on a four to eight-foot stem, with palmately-lobed leaves, and you have a fair mental picture of a papaya plant. The fruits are variable in size, shape, and quality. The external color is green to yellow. The taste of a good ripe papaya is very similar to that of a muskmelon. Papayas, both the fruits and leaves, contain an enzyme[4] called papain, which is capable of digesting protein. (Pineapple juice has some of this property, too.) South Americans often wrap a piece of meat in papaya leaves before cooking it to tenderize it. I have seen birds greedily eating pieces of papaya laves, which probably help them to digest their food. Papaya extract finds commercial use in clarifying beer. It simply digests the yeast cells and any other protein present. Papaya extract is also used in commercial meat tenderizers. There are several related species of papaya, some of them rather edible.

Barbados is a small island somewhat south and east of Martinique in the Caribbean. From the botanical standpoint the island has made

---

[3]Kapok is obtained from another tree in this family.

[4]Enzymes are chemicals capable of digesting or solubilizing food. These are secreted by all living organisms in connection with nutrition.

an impression way out of proportion to its 160-odd square miles of area. There is Barbados lily, Barbados nut, Barbados pride (two lively flowering legume bushes), Barbados cherry and Barbados gooseberry. The Barbados cherry may be either *Eugenia uniflora* in the family Myrtaceae or *Malpighia punicifolia* in the family Malpighiaceae. The three-lobed fruits of the latter are tart, fragrant, and juicy, and can be eaten raw, used for beverage, or stewed. (The related semeruco grows in northern South America.) Only recently has the very high vitamin C content of these small red fruits been discovered.

The Barbados gooseberry is the fruit of a cactus in the genus *Pereskia. Peresekia* is the one rather normal genus of the cactus family, growing as trees with woody stems and true leaves. (Although there is one rather small species, *Pereskia* species in tropical America may grow as trees with a trunk diameter of eighteen inches.) Barbados cherries are also called Barbados gooseberries at times, and also Surinam cherry and Cape gooseberry. There is still another fruit known as Surinam cherry, so the whole thing becomes a bit confusing. That's where scientific names come in handy.

The list of fruits in the family Myrtaceae, the family of the true myrtle and the clove, is too long to permit more than a bare introduction. One of these, guava, is native to southern Florida. Have you ever tasted guava jelly? The jelly is better than the fruits by far. Another fine fruit in this family is rose apple. Eating one of them is like eating rose perfume. The beautiful deep-red Malay apple is rather tart to eat raw, although some people, including myself, are very fond of them. Cooked for sauce they're delicious. The names for these two fruits in South America are pomarosa and pomagas respectively. I know a place in the mountains of Venezuela where, in season, one can gather bushels of pomagas. Rose apples and Malay apples are Asiatic fruits, but have become naturalized in many parts of tropical America.

What are the very best fruits in the world? That, of course, would depend on taste. A peach at its very best, or an apple that snaps right back at you when you bite into it wouldn't be far from the top. One authority who bases his opinion on world-wide experience says that the three best fruits of the world are the pineapple, the mangosteen, and the cherimoya. Another authority says that of these the cherimoya is the very best. On the basis of my own experience I certainly will not disagree with him. I hope that you may be so fortunate as to taste all of them during your lifetime.

INCLUDED IN THIS CHAPTER
GENERA AND FAMILIES OF FRUITS

Plant	Scientific Name	Family
Akee	*Blighia sapida*	Sapindaceae
Almond	*Prunus communis*	Rosaceae
Anon	*Annona reticulata*	Annonaceae
Apple	*Pyrus coronaria*	Rosaceae
Apricot	*Prunus Armeniaca*	Rosaceae
Avocado	*Persea americana*	Lauraceae
Banana	*Musa paradisiaca*	Musaceae
Barbados Cherry	*Eugenia uniflora* or	Myrtaceae
	Malpighia punicifolia	Malpighiaceae
Barbados Gooseberry	*Pereskia aculeata*	Cactaceae
Bilimbi	*Averrhoa bilimbi*	Oxalidaceae
Black Sapote,		
see Sapote, Black		
Blueberries	*Vaccinium* spp.	Ericaceae
Boabab,		
see Monkey Bread		
Cacao (Cocoa,	*Theobroma cacao*	Sterculeaceae
Chocolate)		
Calamondin	*Citrus mitis*	Rutaceae
Carambola	*Averrhoa carambola*	Oxalidaceae
Cashew	*Anacardium occidentale*	Anacardiaceae
Cassaba	*Cucumis melo*	Cucurbitaceae
Cassabanana	*Sicana odorifera*	Cucurbitaceae
Castaño	*Pachira insignis*	Bombacaceae
Ceriman	*Monstera deliciosa*	Araceae
Cherimoya	*Annona Cherimola*	Annonaceae
Cherry, Sour	*Prunus avium*	Rosaceae
Cherry, Sweet	*Prunus cerasus*	Rosaceae
Cranberry	*Oxycoccus. macrocarpon*	Ericaceae
	(*Vaccinium macrocarpon*)	
Currant	*Ribes* spp.	Saxifragaceae
Currant (Dried)	*Vitis,* spp.	Vitaceae
Curuba	*Sicana odoriferra*	Cucurbitaceae
Dates	*Phoenix dactylifera* and	Palmaceae
	several other species	
Dewberry	*Rubus flagellaris* and	Rosaceae
	other species	
Durian	*Durio zibethinus*	Bombacaceae
Genip, see Mamon		

Plant	Scientific Name	Family
Gooseberry	*Ribes grossularia*	Saxifragaceae
Granadillo	*Passiflora quadrangularis*	Passifloraceae
Grapes	*Vitis* spp.	Vitaceae
Grapefruit	*Citrus paradisi*	Rutaceae
Guamo	*Inga* spp.	Leguminosae
Guanabana	*Annona muricata*	Annonaceae
Guava	*Psidium guajava*	Myrtaceae
Huckleberries	*Vaccinium* spp.	Ericaceae
Jujube	*Zizyphus jujuba*	Rhamnaceae
Juneberry	*Amelanchier canadensis*	Rosaceae
Kaffir Orange	*Strychnos spinosa*	Loganiaceae
Kumquat	*Fortunella* spp.	Rutaceae
Lemon	*Citrus limonia*	Rutaceae
Lime	*Citrus aurantifolia*	Rutaceae
Lychee, Litchi	*Nephelium litchi* and *N. chinensis*	Sapindaceae
Malay Apple	*Eugenia malaccensis*	Myrtaceae
Mammee Sapote	*Calocarpum mammosum*	Sapotaceae
Mamey Apple	*Mammea americana*	Guttiferae
Mamon, Mamoncillo	*Melicocca bijuga*	Sapindaceae
Mango	*Mangifera indica*	Anacardiaceae
Mangosteen	*Garcinia mangostana*	Guttiferae
Manirote	*Annona purpurea*	Annonaceae
Mayapple	*Podophyllum peltatum*	Berberidaceae
Maypop	*Passiflora incarnata*	Passifloraceae
Monkey Bread	*Adansonia digitata*	Bombacaceae
Muskmelon	*Cucumis melo* varieties	Curcurbitaceae
Natal Plum	*Carissa grandiflora*	Apocynacae
Nispero	*Achras zapota*	Sapotaceae
Orange, Sour	*Citrus Aurantium*	Rutaceae
Orange, Sweet	*Citrus sinensis*	Rutaceae
Otaheite Gooseberry	*Phyllanthus acidus*	Euphorbiaceae
Papaya	*Carica papaya*	Caricaceae
Parcha	*Passiflora quadrangularis*	Passifloraceae
Passion Fruits	*Passiflora* spp.	Passifloraceae
Pawpaw	*Asimina triloba*	Annonaceae
Peach	*Prunus persica*	Rosaceae
Peach Palm	*Guilielma gasipaes*	Palmaceae
Pear	*Pyrus communis*	Rosaceae
Pejibaye, see Peach Palm		

Plant	Scientific Name	Family
Persimmon, Japanese	*Diospyros kaki*	Ebenaceae
Pinanona, *see* Ceriman		
Pineapple	*Ananas comosus* (*Ananas sativus*)	Bromeliaceae
Pistachio Nut	*Pistacia vera*	Anacardiaceae
Pitajalla, Pitajaya	*Cactus* species	Cactaceae
Plum	*Prunus domestica* and other species	Rosaceae
Pomagas, *see* Malay Apple		
Pomarosa, *see* Rose Apple		
Pomegranate	*Punica granatum*	Punicaceae
Pomelo, *see* Shaddock		
Pond Apple	*Annona glabra*	Annonaceae
Prickly Pears	*Opuntia* spp.	Cactaceae
Quince, Chinese	*Chaenomeles sinensis*	Rosaceae
Quince, Common	*Cydonia oblonga*	Rosaceae
Raspberry, Blackcap	*Rubus occidentalis*	Rosaceae
Raspberry, European	*Rubus idaeus* and other species	Rosaceae
Rose Apple	*Eugenia jambos*	Myrtaceae
Saguaro, Sahuaro		Cactaceae
Sapodilla, *see* Nispero		
Semeruco	*Malpighia glabra*	Malpighiaceae
Sapote, Black	*Diospryos Ebenaster*	Ebenaceae
Sapote, White	*Casimiroa edulis*	Rutaceae
Sea Grape	*Coccolobis uvifera*	Polygonaceae
Shaddock	*Citrus maxima*	Rutaceae
Spanish Lime, *see* Mamon		
Strawberry	*Fragaria* spp.	Rosaceae
Sweetsop, *see* Guanabana		
Tamarind	*Tamarindus indica*	Leguminosae
Tangerine (included here are King and satsuma Oranges)	*Citrus nobilis*	Rutaceae
Tuna	*Opuntia tuna* (applied to other species also)	Cactaceae

Plant	*Scientific Name*	*Family*
White Sapote, see Sapote, White		
Whortleberries	*Vaccinium* spp.	Ericaceae
Wintergreen	*Gaultheria procumbens*	Ericaceae

CHAPTER 10

Odor in Plants

ODORS are very important in our lives, in flowers, food, and perfumes. They are also important in the processes of the plants that produce them. One use is the attracting of insects that will pollinate the flowers.

Plants and plant products are by far the most important means of satisfying man's desire for pleasant odors. In the procuring of these plant materials there has been much history, adventure, gold, misery, and even such prosaic things as technology and industry.

Mankind's interest in odoriferous plants goes back far beyond the beginnings of recorded history. This is evident from the fact that the earliest written records show an extensive knowledge of them and their uses. For example, it is recorded that Merodach-Baladan II, who ruled Babylon from 721 to 710 B.C. and again from 703 to 702 B.C., had a garden in which garlic, onion, thyme, dill, coriander, saffron, and cardamom[1] were grown. It is known that the Babylonians also used cumin, fennel, sesame, and origanum. Not only were these and other species used in cookery and in flavoring drinks, but also in medication and along with other fragrant materials, in perfumes, in ointments for the body, and in sacrificial offerings to the gods. The Bible has many references to spices and other fragrant materials. The earliest of these is in connection with Joseph who supposedly lived around 1700 B.C. It is recorded that his brothers sold him to "a company of Ishmaelites" come "from Gilead with their camels bearing spicery and balm and myrrh, going to carry it down to Egypt" (Gen. 37:25).

Thus we can see that the spice trade was well established early. The demand came almost entirely from royalty, the wealthy, and

---

[1]A table of the species and condiment plants with their scientific names and families may be found at the end of this chapter. Plants mentioned in the chapter, other than species and condiments, are listed in a second table.

the priests. Poor people in those times were fortunate if they could get enough to eat, to say nothing about spices. It was the demand for spices that opened up trade between Asia Minor, Egypt and the Mediterranean region. Later, Europe and other parts of the world established trade with the spice-producing lands to the east. The story of that trade through the ages is a book in itself and has been capably told elsewhere.[2] However, it is interesting that the trade was firmly in the hands of the Arabs until the great pressure to get into this profitable business induced Portugal to send Vasco de Gama around the Cape of Good Hope in 1497.

The Portuguese managed to wrest control of the spice trade from the Arabs and demanded such prices that the Dutch sent Cornelius van Houten around Good Hope in 1595 to see what could be done. After considerable bloodshed the trade came under the control of the Dutch in the East Indies, with the British pushing in to center their trade in India. This same pressure for control of the spice trade drove Columbus to seek a northwest passage and so to discover North America in 1497, and Magellan to pass through the strait named after him and circumnavigate the globe in his three-year voyage that started in 1519. (Magellan himself was killed in the Philippines.) The quest for spices has had, obviously, a profound influence on history.

All odoriferous materials owe their fragrance to their chemical action on the olfactory nerves of the nose. The ability of some of these chemicals to cause reaction of the olfactory nerves is almost beyond belief. The nose can detect ionone, found in violets, at five-billionth gram per cubic meter of air (or about thirteen-billionth ounce per cubic yard). You may have read that the "spice islands" of the East Indies can be smelled long before land is sighted. Some of the evil odors of plants are just as vigorous. For example, when the Brazilian tree, *Gallesia integrifolia* (in the pokeweed family) is cut, the whole forest is permeated with the odor of garlic.

The odor of plants is due to chemicals called essential oils. These are a large group of water-insoluble compounds, fragrant or not so fragrant, secreted by plants, which may be obtained from plants by distillation and other means. They are different, chemically, from common vegetable oils, such as olive oil. The vegetable oils are low in volatility and cannot be distilled from

---

[2]See, for example, *The Story of Spices* by John W. Parry, published by the Chemical Publishing Company, New York City.

the plants. The chemistry of some of these essential oils will be treated somewhat briefly later in the chapter.

Did you ever chew the tender new leaves of the wintergreen plant? This plant, also known as checkerberry or teaberry (*Gaultheria procumbens*), is a member of the enormous heath family. The black, cherry, or sweet birch (*Betula lenta*)of the eastern United States is not at all related to the wintergreen. However, its twigs contain the same fragrant ingredient, methyl salicylate, the chief component of the essential oil occurring in wintergreen. Oil of wintergreen used to be distilled commercially from the leaves of the wintergreen plant or from black birch twigs. It may still be so obtained; however, practically all of it is now obtained chemically from coal tar products. If carefully prepared, the synthetic product is even purer than the natural product. The synthetic product can be prepared at a cost with which the natural material could never compete. Synthetic products are sometimes inferior to the natural oils, however. Some of them contain small amounts of impurities, difficult to remove, that render them less desirable. On the other hand, the natural oil may be a mixture of chemicals exceedingly difficult to reproduce in the laboratory. An example of the latter case is that of attar (or otto) of roses. The natural product is superior to any synthetic mixture yet prepared. Obviously, where this is the case, the natural oils, if one can afford them, are preferred.

Some of the essential oils are irritant in pure form, as anyone who has ever gotten turpentine on the more tender parts of his body well knows. I once took a small bottle of oil of anise with me on a fishing jaunt when I was a boy because it was supposed to make the bait irresistible to fish. I never had a chance to find out whether it would work or not because the stopper came out of the bottle and the oil blistered my seat in no uncertain terms. My friend Dr. George Goodman was once hired by a government agency to gather seeds of certain plants to be used in connection with conservation practices. One of these was a species of *Xanthoxylum* (prickly ash, related to *Citrus*) native to the arid Southwest. At first glance, collecting these seeds looked simple. The trees were covered with the small glandular fruits (they look like minute limes). Dr. Goodman and his companion spread tarpaulins under the trees, got some stout sticks, and began pounding. Almost immediately they beat a hasty retreat. The turpentinelike oil liberated from the bruised fruit was choking. They finally got the seeds by holding their breaths. dashing in, beating the trees, then retreating for fresh air and waiting for the air to clear. These two collectors were pretty well incapacitated after their day's work.

As previously stated, the odor of flowers attracts insects that will pollinate them. Quite a number of flowers, instead of secreting pleasant perfumes that will attract bees, butterflies, and the like, have evil odors that are attractive to carrion-loving insects. A good example is the carrion flower or starfish flower (name due to its shape). Its odor is so bad that carrion flies will lay eggs on it. However, this is mild compared to the unbelievable parasitic Rafflesia flowers of Malaya. This largest of all the flowers is a yard across, with horrid, mottled petals; it has an odor like a dead animal. The flower springs almost directly from the soil, with its haustoria, which parasites use in place of roots, sunk into the roots of the woody vine from which it draws sustenance. The plumlike seeds of the widely planted ginkgo tree (*Ginkgo biloba*) reek with butyric acid which has the odor of very rancid butter.

The attractant and repellant properties of essential oils are frequently useful to man. Many people know of the use of oil of anise around dovecotes to attract more pigeons, and of oil of citronella grass in repelling mosquitoes. There is more on this subject in Chapter 17.

The essential oils are among those products that the plant physiologist would term "differentiative." The formation of differentiative products is dependent on a number of factors: age of plant, temperature, moisture supply, day length, injury, and the like. The gum forming on wounds on cherry trees is an example of the last-named factor, as is the wounding of pitch pine trees to produce exudate in the turpentine industry. In general, conditions that do not encourage vegetative growth favor the formation of differentiative products, as anyone who has tasted turnips grown in hot weather can testify. Procuring the largest quantity of highest quality differentiative product is often quite an art. The *Bursera* species that yield lignaloe are carefully wounded on the trunk to encourage oil formation. Sometimese natural wounding is involved. For example, Borneo camphor is deposited in cysts left by borers in the wood. The tree concerned is *Dryobalanops aromatica*.

It is interesting to the student of botany that the occurrence of essential oils is general in certain plant families — and rare in others. Among the families where essential oils are commonly encountered are the mints (Labiatae), the ginger family (Zingiberaceae), the pine relatives (Pinacae), the citrus group (Rutaceae), the sassafras, cinnamon, camphor family (Lauraceae), plants related to myrtle, clove, and *Eucalyptus* (Myrtaceae), the several magnolias, tulip tree, and others (Magnoliaceae), members of the dogbane family, including oleander and frangipani (Apocynaceae), and a large part of the olive, privet, and lilac group (Oleaceae). In all but the last two of these families, much of the whole plant tends to be fragrant. The tropical family, the Burseraceae, previously mentioned, would find a place in this list as would several others. Members of the carrot family, the Umbelliferae, while not usually characterized by fragrant flowers, are commonly aromatic, and consequently the herbs, or even more commonly the "seeds" (they are, botanically, fruits) frequently find use for flavoring food. Dill, parsley, anise, coriander, and celery are examples.

Odor is basic to pleasant flavor of our foods. We can taste by mouth only sweet, sour (acid), bitter, and salt. Beyond this we can detect certain things by general chemical sense, for example, some of the constituents of pepper, mustard, and horse radish. But most of our "tasting," as you probably know, is done with the nose. A fruit may please us by its appearance, its texture, or consistency, its sweetness and its degree of acidity, and its aroma. Of all of these I contend that aroma is the most important factor in leading us to include fruit in our diet. Otherwise there would not be hundreds of varieties of apples, and a demand for many other kinds of fruits.

In a previous chapter it was noted that one of the muskmelons (*Cucumis melo* var. *dudaim,* the pomegranate melon) is so fragrant that its fruits are used in perfumery. The perfume industry, which to a large extent now depends on synthetic materials, was founded on plant products. Some of the names, such as frankincense and myrrh, are ancient to our civilization. Even today many plants still play an extremely important part in this great industry. For example, oil of ginger, sandalwood, and patchouli[3] are so complex that they have never been successfully duplicated synthetically. In many cases the synthetics have in no way decreased the demand for the natural product. Thus, although artificial essence of violet, ionone, is made in large amounts synthetically, more natural essence of violet is being marketed now than ever before.

The perfume trade (and the spice trade as well) has often been far in advance of science in relation to plant sources. Oil of rhodium was long imported from the Canary Islands from an un-

---

[3]Patchouli is derived from several Asiatic mints, genus *Pogostemon;* the best source is *P. cablin.*

known plant source. Scientists finally found that it was distilled from *Convolulus scoparius,* a relative of the morning glory. The demand for this oil, which has an odor similar to Damascus rose, led to such ungoverned exploitations that the supply is now exhausted.

Several South American species of *Plumeria* furnish frangipani. This material, much used in perfumery, was supposedly first introduced to Europe by one Marquis Frangipani, a major general in the armies of Louis XIV.

The myrrh of the Bible seems to have been a mixture of the gum of *Commiphora myrrha* and labdanum, obtained from *Cistus ladaniferus.* The "myrrh" of Europe is different. It is obtained from *Myrrhis odorata.* Frankincense is obtained from a member of the family Burseraceae, *Boswellia carteri* (and other species). The same family also furnishes lignaloe and some of the best elemi. Bergamot (the true bergamot, not the mint), neroli, and several other perfume oils are obtained from *Citrus* species. Jasmine (*Jasminum* spp.) is related to olive and lilac.

The place in which the plant is grown, and the variety also, influence the quality of the essential perfume oil produced. The best ylang ylang (*Canangium odorata*) was originally obtained from the Philippines. It is now obtained from Reunion Island or Comoro Island near Malaggasy (Madagascar). Elemi is derived from several plants, but the Philippine product comes from *Canarium luzonicum.*

Lavender, a mint, has been grown for centuries, and many species, hybrids, and varieties have been selected, suited to different soil and climatic conditions. Thus, in addition to *Lavandula vera* (*Lavandula officinalis*), there is spike lavender *L. spica,* which thrives at low elevations and can stand considerable hot sun, *L. fragrans* and *L. delphinensis* (these two considered by some authorities to be varieties of *L. spica*) suited to dry conditions, and *L. pyrenaica* (considered by some to be a variety of *L. vera*), which does well in the Pyrenees, as well as other forms. English lavender is superior to that grown on the Continent, although a lavender grown in Victoria, Union of South Africa, is also choice. Formerly, the best spearmint oil came from New York and Michigan. Now, however, very little oil of spearmint is produced in New York. At present there are wide fields of spearmint and peppermint in Indiana and Michigan. Russian peppermint is supposed to be especially fine.

Because these fragrant oils are very delicate materials, time and methods of gathering and handling are sometimes extremely important. Many oils can be obtained simply and cheaply by steam distillation of plants. In this process steam is run through the plant material and the essential oils are carried over into a condenser with the steam. Some oils are decomposed by this method, however, and must be extracted by other means. Many of the citrus peel oils are prepared by squeezing the peel against a sponge. The more delicate oils were formerly extracted by a process known as enfleurage. The flowers were laid on trays over mutton or pork fat. After the flowers had ceased to produce essence, they were replaced by others. Finally, the essential oil was distilled from the fat. The amount of essential oil obtained by this means is sufficient to indicate that the flowers continue to produce their essences after they have been picked.

Enfleurage, as a method for obtaining the more delicate essences, has now been replaced by solvent extraction methods. The solvents used include propylene and butylene. These chemicals are gases at ordinary temperatures and pressures, and for this reason the extractions are performed under sufficient pressure and low enough temperature to liquify the solvent. The high volatility of the solvent makes it certain that all will evaporate at lower pressure, leaving the essential oils. Following evaporation, the solvent is again liquefied under pressure and reused.

One of the oddest methods of gathering plant oils and resins is used for ladanum or labdanum from *Cistus ladaniferus* and related species in the Mediterranean region. The sticky resin adheres to the fleece of sheep and goats, and is raked from the fleece with special tools. However, it is admitted that material obtained directly from the plants is superior.

Strange to say, most of the fixatives used in perfumes are of animal origin, for example, ambergris, secreted by whales, civet from civet cats in Ethiopia, and musk from musk deer in the Himalayas. An exception is ambrette, an expensive material obtained from the seeds of *Hibiscus abelmoschus,* widely cultivated in the Oriental tropics. Fixatives make the pleasant odors of the perfumes more noticeable. They themselves usually have a bad odor.

Many woods are fragrant and are much sought for chests, drawer linings, incense, and even perfumery. Probably the most glamourous name among the fragrant woods is sandlewood. The several species of these more or less parasitic plants are widely distributed through the Asiatic and Australasiatic tropics. There are even related New World plants yielding sandalwood oil. The true sandalwood, *Santalum album,* is native to India. However, in fairly early times this plant was so thoroughly exploited that supplies became limited. In 1778 Hawaiian sandalwood came into world trade; and King Kamehameha the Great was able, in a very few years, to lead his people from barbarism to a considerable degree of civilization on the basis of this trade. The people paid their taxes in sandalwood (called *iliahi* by the Hawaiians), and the king held monopoly on the trade. This paid about $400,000 in one year.

By 1840 the naturally occurring Hawaiian sandalwood was exhausted, and it was necessary to import seed of *Santalum album* from India to re-establish the trade. *Santalum album* is now cultivated in India and other parts of the world. Robinson Crusoe's island[4], Mas-a-Tierra, off the coast of Chile, was once a source of sandalwood; but again the supply was mined rather than cultivated, and the last sandalwood tree on the island died in 1916. At present sandalwood is one of the most valuable woods in the world.

Bois de rose femelle was formerly obtained from French Guiana. This fragrant wood was eagerly sought early in the nineteenth century by European cabinet makers who used it for drawer linings. The botanical source, *Aniba roseodora,* was not named scientifically until 1930. Now the source of bois de rose femelle is the deep interior of Brazil and in the area around the Peruvian-Brazilian border.

In our own country red cedar (which is really a juniper, *Juniperus virginiana*) is commonly used for chests and for closet linings. The wood of Port Orford cedar (*Chamaecyparis lawsoniana*) has a delightful odor. If you work with woods, plan to line something with it sometime. Many other fragrant woods are used as sources of essential oils. Camphor (*Cinnamonum camphora*), many trees in the family Burseraceae (including several species of *Amyris*) several legumes, and *Bulnesia sarmienti* are examples. The Chinese use *Persea* (*Phoebe*) *nanmu* (Lauraceae) in making caskets.

Mankind searches the world for fragrant flowers and shrubs for his gardens. Such collecting has been going on for a very long time. Moctezuma II, once the Aztec emperor of Mexico, led his nation into war to obtain a lovely and fragrant shrub, *Bourreria huanita,* for his famous gardens. It is recorded that Queen Hatshepsut sent an expedition down the east coast of Africa about 1400 B.C. to bring back certain fragrant trees for her garden. The trees

---

[4]Although Robinson Crusoe was a fictional character, the island of Mas-a-Tierra has become associated with the story.

she sought were the source of frankincense. These are members of Burseraceae, a family from which, as we have seen, many perfume and incense oils are obtained.

Garden flowers lacking odor have a handicap in comparison with those that are fragrant. In the past it has been one of the vexations of their growers that gladiolus lacked odor. In recent years a few odoriferous gladioli have been introduced to the trade. The next time you are in an iris garden, observe that different varieties have different perfumes. Many varieties, however, are without odor.

The reader may wish to learn something of the chemistry of odoriferous plants. Obviously all plant odors are due to chemicals secreted by plants, and for many of these essential oils the chemical structure is known. Although one would have to be a specialist in certain fields of organic (carbon) chemistry to qualify as an expert in essential oils, it is interesting to take a passing glance at the structure or pattern of a few of these substances. By way of introduction, the carbon atom has the peculiar ability to hold onto atoms of many other elements, and other carbon atoms to form complex patterns. We will use chemical "shorthand" (symbols) to construct some of these. The elements with which we are concerned are carbon (C), oxygen (O), hydrogen (H), nitrogen (N), and sulfur (S).

Methyl salicylate, the oil of wintergreen, has the structure shown
$$H$$
in Figure 23. The methyl part of it is that $-$ C–H attached to the
$$H$$
right side. The rest of the pattern is most of a salicylic acid structure.[5]

Figure 23

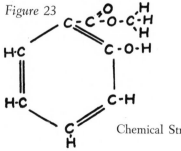

Chemical Structure of Oil of
Wintergreen (Methyl Salicylate)

Vanilla extract, obtained from the seed pod of the tropical

---

[5]Many of the modern chemists indicate, instead of double bonds in the ring, a sort of mutual bonding within the ring itself.

orchid *Vanilla planifolia,* is a mixture of chemicals, among which
are vanillin, numerous resins and amino acids. Coumarin, which is

Figure 24

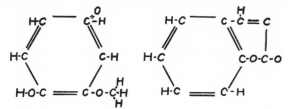

Chemical Structures of Vanillin (left) and Coumarin (right)

sometimes added to synthetic vanilla flavoring, is found in clover
and many other plants. The most important source of courmarin is
the South American tree·*Coumarouna* (or *Dipteryx*) *odorata,* which
is related to clover. Coumarin is obtained from the seed pods of this
tree, which are the tonka beans of commerce. Both vanillin and
coumarin, as in the case of oil of wintergreen, can now be manufactured chemically at relatively small cost. However, many good
cooks still prefer natural vanilla extract.

Closely related in structure to vanillin is oil of cloves, chemically
known as eugenol. The oil is found in the flower buds (the whole

Figure 25

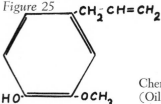

Chemical Structure of Eugenol
(Oil of Cloves)

cloves), of *Eugenia caryophyllata* or *Eugenia aromatica,* native
to the Moluccas in the East Indies. The family is the Myrtaceae. Eugenol occurs in many other plants to which the clove is
not related. Similarly, anethole, one of the principal constituents
of oil of anise, occurs in the seeds of *Pimpinella aromatica,* (P.
anisum), a relative of carrot, and in the seeds of star anise (Illicium
verum), a distant relative of magnolia[6], native to China. Anethole
(or closely related compounds) is also found in many other plants,
including sweet goldenrod (*Solidago odora*) and tarragon (*Artemisia dracunculus*), both in the daisy family.

---

[6]Illicium was formerly included in the family Magnoliaceae, but the relationship is a bit remote, and it is now placed by many botanists in the family
Illiciaceae.

Figure 26

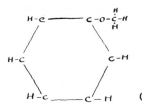

Chemical Structure of Anethole or Anisole

The scent of pine is due to many different compounds and mix-
tures of compounds, varying from species to species. One of these
compounds is pinene. From Figure 27 (Pinene) it may be seen

Figure 27

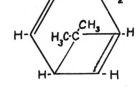

Chemical Structure of Pinene,
One of the Constituents of Pine Oil

that this is a much different pattern than those shown previously
even though there are six carbon atoms in a ring. Pinene is one of
the terpenes, as is limonene, one of the constituents of citrus peel

Figure 28

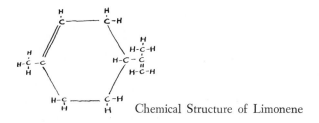

Chemical Structure of Limonene

oil, and menthol, one of the constituents of oils of certain mints.
Camphor, which comes from the camphor tree, *Cinnamomum
camphora*, is also in this group of compounds. The camphor tree is
related to our sassafras tree and to cinnamon. All three are in
Lauraceae, the laurel family. The leaves and the wood of all

members of the laurel family are likely to be odoriferous, although not always pleasantly so, as witness, stinkwood (*Ocotea bullata*) of South Africa. Much camphor is now made synthetically from pine oil. It is not very hard to do. A student I once taught in high-school chemistry went through the process just for fun and made a chunk of camphor as big as two fists from the oil he distilled from an old pine stump.

Figure 29

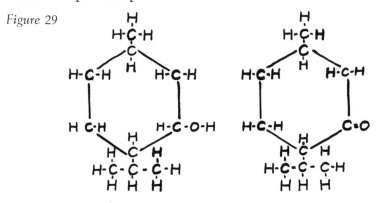

Chemical Structures of Menthol (left) and Menthone (right)

If, in the oil of wintergreen structure, we had an –NH₂ (amine) in place of the OH, as shown in Figure 23, we would have methyl anthranilate, with an odor something like Concord grapes. Methyl

Figure 30

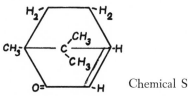

Chemical Structure of Camphor

anthranilate, ethyl butyrate, ethyl acetate and other compounds are responsible for the aroma of blue grapes. I was once experimenting

Chemical Structure of Methyl Anthranilate

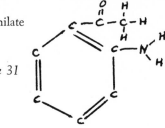

Figure 31

Figure 32

$$
\begin{array}{l}
CH_3{-}\underset{\displaystyle CH_3}{\underset{|}{C}}H{-}CH_2{-}CH_2{-}\underset{\displaystyle CH_3}{\underset{|}{C}}{=}\,CH{-}CH_2OH
\end{array}
$$

Chemical Structure of Geraniol

with methyl anthranilate in a laboratory. The young daughter of a neighbor came in for a visit and decided that it was a very fine thing. I gave her a small bottle of it to take home, but she managed to drop it just as she opened her front door. I felt sorry for her family; their threshold smelled like grape pop for weeks and weeks.

Many of the essential oils do not have a ring structure. Geraniol, found in oil of roses, as well as rose geranium, has the pattern shown in Figure 32. Geraniol is widely distributed in nature. It is one of the constituents of oils obtained from citronella grass, *Andropogon (Cymbopogon) nardus,* and lemon grass, *Andropogon citriodorus.* It even occurs in certain pine oils.

Not all of these essential oils are fit for perfume. The various members of the mustard family and the relatives of onion (species of *Allium*) are examples. The chemical structures of a few of the constituents of the essential oils from these plants are:

$CH_2{=}CH{-}CH_2{-}N{=}C{=}S$, Allyl-Isothiocyanate, found in mustard seed;

$$
\begin{array}{ccccccccc}
H & & H & H & H & & H & & \\
| & & | & | & | & & | & & \\
C & = & C & - & C & - & N & - & C - N \\
| & & & & | & & & & \| \quad | \\
H & & & & H & & & & S \quad H
\end{array}
$$

Allyl Thiocarbimide, found in horse radish root; and

$$
\begin{array}{l}
CH_2{=}CH{-}CH_2 \\
\qquad\qquad\qquad\quad \rangle S \\
CH_2{=}CH{-}CH_2
\end{array}
$$

S, Diallyl Sulfide, found in garlic.

And thus we see that odor in plants is a subject that reaches from the spice and perfume trade to our backyard gardens, from insect repellents to insect attractants, from incense to fragrant woods for chest linings — a very large field indeed.

PARTIAL LIST OF PLANTS USED AS SPICES, CONDIMENTS AND FOR BEVERAGES[7]

Common Name	Scientific Name	Family	Where Native[8]	Remarks
Absinthe	Artemisia Absinthium	Compositae	Europe	Herb used in flavoring liqueurs, e.g., absinthe.
Allspice	Pimenta officinale	Myrtaceae	South America	Named allspice because the fruits have odor resembling several common spices.
Almond	Prunus (Amygdalus) Communis	Rosaceae	Asia	The kernels are the source of both sweet and bitter oil of almonds, depending on variety.
Angelica	Angelica archangelica and A. officinalis	Umbelliferae	Eurasia	The herb is used as meat garnish. The stems are candied. Used also in flavoring the liqueurs chartreuse and vulneraine.
Angostura	Galipea officinalis	Rutaceae	South America	The bark is used in flavoring liqueurs.
Anise	Pimpinella anisum	Umbelliferae	Egypt to Greece	Used in liqueurs, e.g., anisette, and in baked goods and candy.

[7]Many fruits are also used in flavoring foods. As these are listed in the chapter "Fruits of the World," they are not included in this list.

[8]It is not always certain where plants originated. The location cited here is that in which the plant is thought to have been native.

Common Name	Scientific Name	Family	Where Native[8]	Remarks
Anise, Star	Illicium verum	Magnoliaceae or Illiciaceae	China	Used as an anise substitute.
Asafetida	Ferula fetida and other species	Umbelliferae	Eastern Mediterranean	Used in the near East as far as Persia, at least, in gravies.
Balm, Lemon Balm	Melissa officinalis	Labiatae	Eurasia	The leaves are used in cooking and for a tea.
Basil, Sweet	Ocimum Basilicum	Labiatae	Old World Tropics	The leaves are used in cookery.
Bay	Laurus nobilis	Lauraceae	Mediterranean Region	The leaves are used in cookery.
Bergamot,[9] Orange Mint	Mentha citrata	Labiatae	Eurasia	The leaves are used in cookery.
Birch, Sweet	Betula nigra	Betulaceae	North America	Twigs with wintergreen flavor.
Borage	Borago officinalis	Boraginaceae	Mediterranean	Used to flavor beverages. The flowers are used for garnish.
Cacao, Chocolate	Theobroma cacao	Sterculiaceae	South America	The seeds are the source of cocoa and chocolate. They have been used as money.

[9]Do not confuse with oil of bergamot obtained from the peel of the bergamot orange, or with wild bergamot, *Monarda mollis*, a mint native to North America.

Common Name	Scientific Name	Family	Where Native[8]	Remarks
Caraway	Carum Carvi	Umbelliferae	Europe	Caraway "seed"[10] are used in flavoring cookies, cakes, etc. A liqueur is flavored with it.
Cardamom	Elettaria cardamomum	Zingiberaceae	India	The "seeds" are used in pickles, etc.
Cassia	Cinnamomum cassia	Lauraceae	Asia, Australia	Cassia "buds" (young fruits) are used as cinnamon substitute. The bark is also so used.
Cayenne Pepper — see Chile Pepper				
Celery	Apium graveolens var. dulce.	Umbelliferae	Mediterranean	The "seeds" are used in pickles, etc.
Cherry Bark	Prunus serotina, P. virginiana	Rosaceae	North America	The bark is used in flavoring beverages.
Chervil, Salad Chervil	Anthriscus cerefolium	Umbelliferae	Southeast Europe S. Asia	Used in salads and as a garnish.
Chicory, Succory	Cichorium Intybus	Compositae	Probably India	The root is used in coffee, sometimes used as an adulterant.

---

[10]Many so-called "seeds" are fruits with seeds enclosed, from the botanical point of view.

Common Name	Scientific Name	Family	Where Native[8]	Remarks
Chile Pepper	Capsicum fruitescens (Solanum annuum)	Solanaceae	South America	Paprika and red or cayenne pepper are prepared from the dried, ground fruits of varieties of peppers. These and sweet pepper are not related to black pepper nor to the pepper tree.
China Tea — see Tea				
Chives	Allium schoenoprasum	Liliaceae	Eurasia	The leaves are used in salads, etc.
Chocolate — see Cacao				
Cinnamon (also see Cassia)	Cinnamomum zeylanicum	Lauraceae	Ceylon	The bark has been used for flavoring since ancient times. Somewhere between 1765 and 1770 de Kok, a colonist in Ceylon, aided by Falck (then governor of Ceylon) established the first cinnamon plantation, which was very successful.

Common Name	Scientific Name	Family	Where Native[8]	Remarks
Citron[11]	Citrus medica	Rutaceae	Asia, probably China	The candied peel is used in cakes, etc.
Clary	Salvia sclarea	Labiatae	South Europe	The leaves are used for seasoning and in flavoring certain white wines and liqueurs.
Cloves	Eugenia aromatica	Myrtaceae	Probably Moluccas	The flower buds are used for spice. Probably cloves were not introduced into Europe until after the Portuguese discovered the Moluccas.
Cocoa — see Cacao				
Coffee	Coffea arabica and other species[12]	Rubiaceae	Tropic Africa	The well-known coffee of commerce.
Cola	Cola acuminata	Sterculiaceae	Tropic Africa	The seeds are the source of a flavoring used in many soft drinks. The plant is a tree.

[11]Not to be confused with one form of watermelon.
[12]Liberian coffee is Coffea liberica. Zanzibar coffee is Coffea zanguebariae.

Common Name	Scientific Name	Family	Where Native[8]	Remarks
Coriander	Coriandrum sativum	Umbelliferae	South Europe	The "seeds" are the centers of the old-fashioned candies called jawbreakers.
Coumarin — see Tonka beans				
Cumin	Cuminum Cyminum	Umbelliferae	Mediterranean	Used in cookery and pickling.
Curry Leaves	Murraya koenigii	Rutaceae	Tropic Asia	One of several ingredients in curry powder.
Curry Powder —	This is a combination of several condiments including curry leaves, turmeric, garlic, ginger, black pepper, etc.			
Dill	Anethum graveolens	Umbelliferae	Europe (Asia also?)	Used in cookery and in making pickles. Both herb and "seeds" are used.
Fennel	Foeniculum vulgare (F. officinale)	Umbelliferae	South Europe	Used in cookery (fish). The stems are candied and a liqueur is prepared from the "seeds."
Fenugreek	Trigonella foenum-graecum	Leguminosae	South Europe	Seeds used to flavor bread and fatten young ladies for marriage in S. Africa.
Garlic	Allium sativum	Liliaceae		Used since ancient times for flavoring, often with meats and fish.

Common Name	Scientific Name	Family	Where Native[8]	Remarks
Geranium, Rose	Pelargonium graveolens	Geraniaceae	Africa	The leaves are used, for example, in apple jelly.
Ginger	Zingiber officinale	Zingiberaceae	Asia	The dried root is used as a spice. The candied root is a confection.
Grains of Paradise	Amomum granum-paradisi	Scitaminaceae (Zingiberaceae, according to some authorities)	East Indies	Used as a pepper substitute and in beverages.
Horehound	Marrubium vulgare	Labiatae	Eurasia	Used in candy and, in some regions, to flavor beer.
Hops	Humulus lupulus	Cannibinaceae	Eurasia	The fruits ("cones") are used to flavor beer and sometimes in bread-making.
Horse Radish	Armoracia rusticana	Cruciferae	Eastern Mediterranean	The ground root is used with meats, (especially ham.
Hyssop	Hyssopus officinale	Labiatae	South Eurasia	The leaves are used to flavor soup.
Jasmine, Jessamine	Jasminum officinale	Oleaceae	Persia	The flowers are used to flavor tea, and also in perfume.

Common Name	Scientific Name	Family	Where Native[8]	Remarks
Juniper Berries	Juniperus communis J. virginiana and other species (J. virginiana is our common red cedar.)	Pinaceae	Temperate regions of Old and New World.	The berries are used to flavor gin and in cookery.
Lemon	Citrus limonia	Rutaceae	China or India (not certain)	The candied peel used in cookery. The peel oil is also used. The juice is, of course, used in lemonades, etc.
Licorice	Glycyrrhiza glabra	Leguminosae	Mediterranean Region	Used in licorice candy and to disguise flavor of medicine. Some use in chewing tobacco. Many black candies are not flavored with licorice but rather with anise.
Lime	Citrus aurantifolia	Rutaceae	India or East Asia	The small, lemon-like fruits are used for beverages.
Lovage	Levisticum officinale	Umbelliferae	South Europe	Used, with tansy and yarrow, to make lovage cordial. Used in candies.

Common Name	Scientific Name	Family	Where Native[8]	Remarks
Mace	Myristica fragrans	Myristicaceae	Moluccas	The outer hull of nutmeg, ground, is mace. White mace is obtained from *M. otoba*. Other species furnish mace. It is used in pies, cakes, puddings, etc.
Maple	Acer saccharum	Aceraceae	North America	Maple syrup is used to flavor candies. Artificial maple flavorings are prepared also.
Marjorum, Sweet	Majorana hortensis	Labiatae	South Europe	The leaves are used in soups, stews, etc.
Mate, Paraguay Tea	Ilex paraguariensis	Aquifoliaceae	Southern South America	The standard tea for large areas of South America.
Mint, Apple	Mentha rotundifolia	Labiatae	Europe	Used to flavor drinks, jellies, etc.
Mint, Cultivated	M. arvensis	Labiatae	Of wide distribution in many varieties.	Source of mint flavoring. The Japanese variety *piperascens* is very rich in oil.

Common Name	Scientific Name	Family	Where Native[8]	Remarks
Mustard, Black	Brassica nigra (Sinapis nigra)	Cruciferae	Old World	The seeds are the principal source of table mustard. They are also used in pickling and cookery.
Mustard, White	B. alba (S. alba)	Cruciferae	Old World	Used for much the same purposes as black mustard.
Myrtle	Myrtus communis	Myrtaceae	Mediterranean Region	The fruits are used as a condiment.
Nutmeg	Myristica fragrans	Myristicaceae	Moluccas	The ground seed is used to flavor cakes, puddings, etc. These were once faked in United States — the "Connecticut nutmeg," was made of wood and touched with a bit of oil of nutmeg.
Orange	Citrus sinensis (sweet orange) C. aurantium (sour orange)	Rutaceae	South China or Cochin China	The juice is used in beverages; the peel is candied and used in baked goods. The peel oil is also used.
Paprika — see Chile Powder Paraguay Tea — see Mate				

Common Name	Scientific Name	Family	Where Native[8]	Remarks
Parsley	Petroselinum crispum (P. hortense) (Apium petroselinum)	Umbelliferae	Europe	This is the well-known garden parsley. It is used in soups, salads, etc., and as a garnish.
Pepper, Black or White	Piper nigrum	Piperaceae	Tropic Asia	This is the common table pepper. White pepper is obtained from the same source. "Peppercorns" in Colonial times were purchased as an investment, as we buy stocks or bonds. Distribution among heirs was carefully specified in wills.
Pepper, Red or Cayenne — see Chile Powder				
Peppermint	Mentha piperita (common) M. arvensis (especially Japanese variety piperascens)	Labiatae	M. piperita, Europe M. arvensis, Eurasia	The oil from the leaves is used in candy, gum, etc.
Pimenta, Pimento — see Allspice				

Common Name	Scientific Name	Family	Where Native[8]	Remarks
Poppy Seed	Papaver somniferum	Papaveraceae	Eurasia	The seeds of the opium poppy are used on bread, in poppy seed rolls, etc.
Rose Geranium — see Geranium				
Rose Petals	Rosa damascena and probably other species	Rosaceae	Asia?	The petals are used in jellies, cake, etc.
Rue (Herb-o'grace)	Ruta graveolens	Rutaceae	East and South Europe	The herb is used in cookery.
Saffron	Crocus sativus	Iridaceae	Asia Minor	The stigmas are used for food coloring and spice.
Sage	Salvia officinalis	Labiatae	Mediterranean	The herb is used to flavor meat and dressing. A tea is made of the leaves.
Sarsaparilla	Smilax spp.	Liliaceae	Mexico to South America	The root is used in flavoring soft drinks.
Sassafras	Sassafras albidum (S. variifolium)	Lauraceae	North America	The bark is used to make a tea and as a flavoring. The root bark is most commonly used.
Sesame	Sesamum indicum	Pedaliaceae	Asia	The seeds are used in or on pastry. A very good salad oil is obtained from sesame seeds.

Common Name	Scientific Name	Family	Where Native[8]	Remarks
Spearmint	Mentha spicata	Labiatae	Europe	Used in gum, candies, on meats, etc.
Summer Savory	Satureja hortensis	Labiatae	Europe	Herb is used in cookery.
Sweet Basil — see Basil, Sweet				
Sweet Birch — see Birch, Sweet				
Tansy, Bitter Buttons	Tanacetum vulgare	Compositae	Europe	Once much used in cakes and omelettes. Used as a tonic.
Tarragon	Artemisia dracunculus	Compositae	Europe	Flavoring, for example, tarragon vinegar.
Tea	Thea sinensis	Theaceae	China, India	The leaves are used for common tea.
Teaberry — see Wintergreen				
Thyme	Thymus vulgaris	Labiatae	South Europe	Used as a flavoring herb and in perfumes.
Thyme, Lemon	T. citriodorus (T. Serpyllum var. vulgaris)	Labiatae	Eastern Mediterranean region	Used much as preceeding.

Common Name	Scientific Name	Family	Where Native[8]	Remarks
Tonka Bean	Coumarouna (Dipteryx) odorata	Leguminosae	Guianas	This is the tonka bean of commerce. It has a flavor much like vanilla and is used as vanilla substitute and in tobacco (snuff).
Turmeric	Curcuma longa	Zingiberaceae	India	The root is one of the ingredients of curry powder. Used also as a pickling spice.
Vanilla	Vanilla Fragrans (V. planifolia)	Orchidaceae	South America	The pods are the source of natural vanilla.
Water Cress	Nasurtium officinale (and other names)	Cruciferae	Europe	The peppery leaves will do much to brighten a tossed salad.
Wintergreen	Gaultheria procumbens	Ericaceae	North America	The leaves contain fragrant oil, methyl salicylate. This is used in candies, etc. The same oil is found in sweet birch twigs (Betula lenta).
Wormwood — see Absinthe				

FAMILIES OF PLANTS FOR GENERA AND SPECIES
IN THIS CHAPTER,
OTHER THAN SPECIES AND CONDIMENTS

Allium species	Onion, etc.	Liliaceae
Andropogon (Cymbopogon) citriodorus	Lemon Grass	Graminae
Andropogon (Cymbopogon) nardus	Citronella Grass	Graminae
Aniba reseodora	Bois de Rose Femelle	Lauraceae
Bourreria huanita	Huanita	Boraginaceae
Bulnesia sarmienti	Palo Santo	Zygophyllaceae
Bursera species	Palo Balsamo	Burseraceae
Canangium odorata	Ylang Ylang	Annonaceae
Canarium luzonicum	Elemi	Burseraceae
Chamaecyparis lawsoniana	Port Orford Cedar	Pinaceae of some authorities, Cupressaceae of others
Cinnamomum camphora	Camphor	Lauraceae
Cistus ladaniferus	Labdanum	Cistaceae
Citrus species		Rutaceae
Commiphora myrrha	Myrrh	Burseraceae
Convolulus scoparius	(Oil of Rhodium from this)	Convolvulaceae
Cucumis melo var. dudaim	Pomegranate Melon	Cucurbitae
Dryobalanops aromatica	Borneo Camphor	Lauraceae
Gallesia integrifolia	(Pokeweed relative)	Phytolaceae
Ginkgo biloba	Ginkgo	Ginkgoaceae
Hibiscus abelmoschus	Musk Mallow	Malvaceae
Juniperus virginiana	Red Cedar, Juniper	Pinaceae
Myrrhis odorata	Myrrh	Umbelliferae
Persea (Phoebe) nanmu		Lauraceae
Plumeria species	Frangipani	Apocynaceae
Pogostemon cablin	Patchouli	Labiatae
Rafflesia sp.	Rafflesia	Rafflesiaceae
Santalum album	Sandalwood	Santalaceae
Solidago odora	Sweet Goldenrod	Compositae
Stapelia asterias	Starfish Flower	Asclepiadaceae
Xanthoxylum sp.	Prickly Ash	Rutaceae

FOR FURTHER READING

Coon, Nelson, *Fragrance and Fragrant Plants for House and Garden;* Diversity, 1967.

Masselman, G., *Money Trees: The Spice Trade;* Mc Graw-Hill.

Parry, John W., *The Story of Spices;* Chemical Publishing Co., 1953.

CHAPTER 11

Borgias of the Plant World

OISONOUS plants have always held a fascination for mankind, and man's knowledge and use of them is ancient. Modern science has discovered few plant sources of poisonous or narcotic substances that have not been long familiar to the common people. Opium poppy, hemp, tobacco, the plant sources of cocaine, the fish and arrow poisons, and others have all been used since time out of mind. Primitive man had both time and reason to become familiar with the plants that surrounded him. He tried to protect himself and his family from starvation, from savage beasts and human enemies, from disease, and from troublesome insects. For many of man's needs, plant poisons are extremely important.

The use of plants as fish poisons has been practiced in many parts of the world, and their use still persists. The fish-poisoning plants are usually crushed and placed in streams or ponds. With several of these plants the fish are merely rendered unconscious. Some, however, actually kill the fish. In either case, the user of fish poisons merely applies his poison, picks up the fish that come floating to the top and carries them home. Scientists have employed this method in studies on fish, although more recently they have used a mild electric shock for the same purpose.

Some sources of fish poison yield "safe" substances, offering no danger that cattle drinking from the stream will be injured or that people eating the fish will be poisoned. In general, certain legumes are in this group. Other plants — for example, many of the *Euphorbia* relatives — are definitely unsafe and are used only when and where better poisons are not available. Fish taken with unsafe poisons are cleaned at once, especially as to removing the gills, to prevent people eating them from being poisoned. The legume poisons are not only safe, as a rule, but if not used in excess will permit recovery of the fish not removed from the stream.

A plant capable of killing or stunning fish may have value as an insecticide. Many of our plant-source insecticides were first used as fish poisons. Derris and cube from *Derris* and *Tephrosia* and rotenone from *Lonchocarpus* species, all of them legumes, are examples. All contain rotenone, deguelin, and related compounds.

Arrow poisons have also been employed in many parts of the world, and in some places they are still used. The Motolone Indians, for example, living in an area on the border of western Venezuela and adjacent Columbia, greet outsiders, even today, with a curare-tipped arrow. A pound of protocurarine, one of the active principles in curare, is sufficient to kill twenty thousand or more people.

Poisoned arrows or darts are used much more commonly for hunting. From a practical standpoint it is a good idea. A man with a blow-gun and a bundle of darts will quietly kill enough birds or animals for his needs with little or no alarm to the remaining game, which is more than a man can do with a gun. In battle or ambush the poisoned dart is equally efficient. A small soundless dart, a stinging sensation, and quick death has been a sequence often repeated.

Many substances used as arrow poisons cause inflamation and blistering rather than death. These are used against enemies, apparently to add insult to injury. Some of these, for example, are relatives of poison ivy. If you have suffered from ivy poisoning, imagine the agony that would be caused by a similar poison well placed under the skin. In some regions opium or a similar substance is used on hunting darts to stupefy the game and prevent its escape while other more toxic substances do their work.

Of all the arrow-poison plants, probably the most deadly species are found in the genera *Acokanthera* and *Strophanthus,* in the dogbane family, *Strychnos* (family Loganiaceae), especially species growing in South America (curare poisons), *Aconitum* species in the buttercup family, and *Antiaris toxicaria* in the mulberry family. Remarkably, *Strychnos* species have been employed as arrow poisons in Asia, Africa, and South America by many different peoples, their use resulting from independent discovery.

There were relatively few plants employed as arrow poisons in North America. In part this may be due to the fact that rattlesnake venom is a very effective arrow poison and was so used. Serpent venom, if available, has been used in all parts of the world. The American aborigines also employed the venom of the black widow spider to stun small game. Poisonous toads, scorpions, spiders, and centipedes find use in many tropical regions. In Malayan streams there are fish with poisonous stingers on their fins, and these are milked for arrow poison. The gall of certain birds and of crocodiles has been employed. In Africa the grubs of certain beetles, when found feeding on poisonous *Euphorbia* species, are used as effective sources of arrow poison by the Hottentots. Even arsenical minerals have been employed. Primitive man wanted results, and he used those substances that proved most effective and readily available.

Many of the families of plants furnishing arrow poisons also furnish fish poisons. If one plant in a family has poisonous properties, there are apt to be other poisonous relatives. Some families of plants are so generally suspect that it is well to assume all of them poisonous unless we know otherwise. Plants with milky sap, for example, dogbane, oleander, snow-on-the-mountain, and poinsettia, are apt to be poisonous; and it is a fair rule to be wary of all plants with milky sap unless one knows them to be harmless. The tendency for children to put things in their mouths makes questionable the wisdom of growing the common snow-on-the-mountain, for example, in a flower garden. There have been cases of death to children who have eaten the leaves. The poisonous substances of caster bean include ricin, present in the coats of the seed. American soldiers stationed in the Philippines hit upon the idea of eating whole caster beans when they needed a physic. The practice was considered satisfactory until a couple of them died.

Toads obtain their food by darting out their tongues at passing insects. Their instinct is to gather in anything that flutters by. Someone once observed a toad snapping up faded oleander blossoms as they fell from the shrub. The toad was dead in a short time. A child could be similarly poisoned.

Some of our foods are obtained from poisonous plants. Cassava meal and tapioca are made from the fleshly root of the tropical plant *Manihot utillissima,* one of the *Euphorbia* or spurge relatives. When raw, the roots of some of the cultivated forms contain hydrocyanic acid, a deadly poison, and the ground or grated root must be carefully heated to drive off all of this acid before the cassava meal can be eaten safely.

In the Caribbean region is found the manzanillo or manchineel, *Hippomane mancinella,* another notorious member of the spurge family. All parts of the plant are poisonous and so is the smoke of the burning wood. The early Spanish explorers mistook the fruits for crabapples and ate some of them. Several of them died, and the rest were thoroughly frightened. Gondalo Fernandez de Oviedo y Valdes warned his king of this tree in his *Natural History of the*

Indies. A portion of the translation of that work, made in 1555 by Richard Eden says:

> The Apples wherewith the Indian Canibales inueneme [envenom] theyre arrowes growe on certeyne trees covered with many braunches and leues [leaves], beinge very greene and growyng thicke. They are laden with an abundance of these euyll [evil] frutes, and haue theyre leues lyke the leues of a pear tree, but that they are lesse and rounder. The frute is much lyke the muscadel peares of the island of Sicillie or Naples in forme and biggenesse: and are in sum partes steyned with redde spottes, and of a very sweete sauoure [savor]. These trees for the most part growe euer [ever] by the sea coastes and neare unto the water: and are so fayre and of pleasaunte sauoure, that theyre is no man that seethe theym but will desyre to eate thereof.... But that your maiestie may the better consyder the force of the venome of these trees, youe shall further understande that yf a man doo but repose him selfe to sleepe a lyttle whyle under the shadow of the same, he hath his head and eyes so swolne when he ryseth that the lyddes are ioyned [joined] with the chekes. And if it chance one droppe or more of the dew of sayde tree to faule into the eye, it utterly destroyeth the syght. The pestilent nature of this tree is such that it can not bee declared in few woordes!!

It should be added that this account is somewhat embellished. The plant, though poisonous, is not *that* bad.

The tendency for poisonous characteristics to be general in a plant family is very well illustrated in the Anacardiaceae. Here belong poison ivy and poison sumac. Poison wood is found in Florida and the Caribbean region, while *Rhus striata,* a related species, grows in Mexico and Central America. In Japan we find the lacquer tree, *Rhus verniciflua,* plants of which have been naturalized in several parts of the United States. Although it is the source of Japanese black lacquer, it is still a poison sumac, and several cases of ivy poisining have been reported by persons who have handled articles finished with this lacquer. Enthusiastic mah jong players of a few years back wondered where they got poison ivy and kept right on playing with the lacquered pieces. Many species of Rhus are non-toxic, for example, the common red-berried sumacs of the northern United States. All of the poisonous species have white berries, a good point to remember.

In the tropics of Asia we find similar vesicant anacardiaceous plants in the genera *Gluta* and *Semecarpus. Gluta renghas* is employed as an arrow poison. The plant is known locally as ringhas, renghas, rangas, or by similar modifications of the name. Some of the species grow into fair-sized trees. The reddish sap is especially poisonous.

The vesicant or blistering action of cashew-nut hulls and mango peel are discussed in the chapter on fruits. Both plants are in Anacardiaceae. The chemical that gives this property to cashew nut hulls is called cardol and has the structure shown in Figure 33.

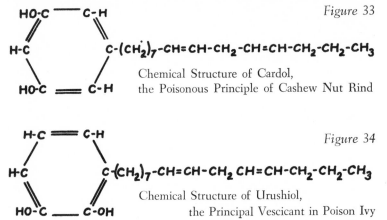

Figure 33

Chemical Structure of Cardol,
the Poisonous Principle of Cashew Nut Rind

Figure 34

Chemical Structure of Urushiol,
the Principal Vescicant in Poison Ivy

Poison ivy contains urushiol, its structure shown in Figure 34. Note that the patterns are similar. Urushiol is what the organic chemist would call a substituted catechol, and both compounds are fairly closely related to carbolic acid. The poisonous substances in the above family are oil soluble. Oily salves should never be used in treatment as they serve to spread it around.

We must bear in mind that all poisons are merely chemicals. The structures of many of them are well known. The basic structures of the alkaloids, which include nicotine from tobacco, cocaine from *Erythroxylon coca,* morphine obtained from poppies, and many others, are of interest because there are obvious threads of similarity between them, even though they are often obtained from widely different plants. All of them contain nitrogen in their structures, and all are bitter. In fact, if anything is bitter, the bitterness is apt to be due to an alkaloid. Some alkaloids are very poisonous (for example, strychnine) while others are not poisonous.

When Serturer prepared pure morphine from opium in 1817, and Pelletier and Caventou isolated strychnine in 1818, they used mild alkali to liberate the pure drug. Asians had been using lime (a mild alkali) with their betel pepper leaf and areca nut (*Areca*

Catechu) for ages, as had the natives of South America with their coca leaves. It would be interesing to know how two primitive peoples on opposite sides of the earth made the same discovery.

The Mexican Indians used pelloté (or peyoté), obtained from *Lophophora williamsii* (a member of the cactus family), to produce intoxication in connection with certain religious ceremonies. The drugs anhaline, pellotine, and others in this preparation, while lethal in overdose, in small doses cause excitement much like that of alcohol, a feeling of dual existence, increased sensitivity to colors, and other symptoms of euphoria, that is, a sense of buoyancy and well being. At the time this was written, there was a court case in the southwestern United States involving the use of this drug by semireligious groups, most of whose members were of Indian ancestry.

The natives of northern South America powdered the pods of the leguminous tree, *Piptadenia peregrina,* and drew the powder into their nostrils to produce intoxication. They used specially made short tubes for this purpose. The local name of this widely distributed and very common tree is cajobo, pronounced *că-hō-bō*. It is very probable that the drug is still used.

In central Asia a mushroom, *Amanita muscaria,* the fly agaric, is used to cause similar intoxication. The same mushroom was used by our teutonic ancestors. Our word "berserk" originated in connection with its use. Eaten prior to battle, it would cause a frenzy in which the user would howl and shriek, froth at the mouth, and in general act like an enraged beast. Such a frenzy was supposed to render the warrior invulnerable in battle — and certainly must have been frightening to his opponents. The word "berserk" came from the roots "ber" (bear) and "serk" (sack or garment). In other words, the intoxicated one "put on the bear skin." This mushroom is common in the United States. If you encounter it, you will recognize it by its fairly large cap, dull orange on top, with whitish, raised flecks. It is related to *Amanita phalloides,* the well-named death angel.

In Asia Minor a secret order of Mohammedans, during the time of the crusaders, employed hashish (which we know as marijuana) to intoxicate themselves prior to committing murder. They were referred to as Hashishians, and from this comes the word "assassin." The same people were also called "tugs" whence our word "thug." The use of marijuana still persists, as we well know, in the United States. (The plant is the source of a hemp.)

Intoxicating and rather poisonous drugs occur in the several

Datura species, such as jimson weed and angel trumpet. They have been widely used by American aborigines, especially in connection with religious ceremonies. The Piutes would bruise and ferment jimson weed seeds and administer the decoction to maidens prior to certain ceremonial dances. Many of the tribes revered the spirit of the jimson weed. If we add to the above list cocaine, opium, and in a somewhat milder sense, tobacco (and there are many others), it is obvious that men have for ages enjoyed doping themselves with such semi-toxic or toxic nerve drugs. Note that often such use is connected with religious ceremonies.

Figure 35

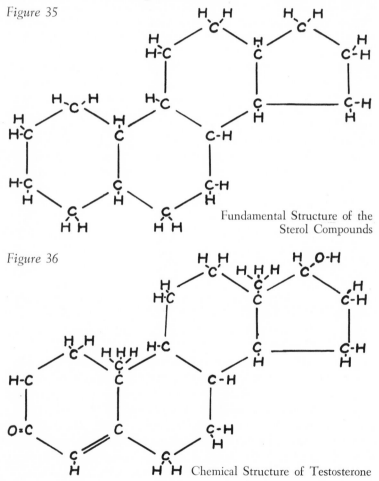

Fundamental Structure of the Sterol Compounds

Figure 36

Chemical Structure of Testosterone

The sterol structure traces an intricate pattern through the plant and animal kingdom. In Figures 35 and 36 the relationship is shown between the basic sterol pattern and that of phenanthrene, found in coal tar. Compare it also to the testosterone pattern. The many sterol compounds are simply chemicals in which different groups are attached to the basic sterol structure. Testosterone is the male sex hormone. The female sex hormone, estrone, has been isolated from certain species of willow. One of the sapogenins (these are found in plants which yield a soapy material), diosgenine, has been converted to the male sex hormone. To the sterol group belong some of the most powerful heart stimulants and poisons, including the digitalis drugs (from plants of genus *Digitalis*), adrenalin (secreted by the adrenal glands), the venom of toad skin (bufotoxin), certain substances such as cholesterole in the bile (I have mentioned that the gall of certain birds and of crocodiles is used as arrow poison), certain of the drugs in the powerful *Strophanthus* poisons, and in the saponins — soaplike plant extracts that are so dangerous because of their ability to disintegrate blood corpuscles. One of these compounds, ergosterol, occurs in the skin. When exposed to sunlight or ultra-violet light, this becomes vitamin D, which prevents and cures rickets in animals, including man. A few of the sterol compounds are capable of inducing cancer. There is considerable interest in certain of the sterols at present because some of them, taken orally, prevent pregnancy.

Many animal sterols are found in plants and vice versa. What is the connection? Some are necessary to our vital processes in small amounts, but are deadly in large amounts. Are the poisonous ones poisonous because their structures, so similiar to that of hormones, enable them to fit into vital processes and upset them so as to cause death in a very short time? This is an interesting question. Part of the answer to this problem may be found in an account of the sterols and their relation to plant poisons by Louis F. Fieser, published in *Scientific American,* January, 1955. This would be a good starting point for anyone wishing to pursue the subject further. There has, however, been considerable additional work on these compounds since that date.

Many garden flowers contain toxic substances if eaten or injected into the blood stream. The *Amaryllis* family is a good example. All of the following members of the family contain poisonous substances: Atamasco lily, narcissus, daffodil, belladonna lily, spider lily, and *Lycoris radiata. Buphane disticha,* one of the arrow poisons, is occasionally grown as an ornamental in this country. Squill, used to poison rats, is still another relative.

Monk's hood, an arrow poison, is sometimes grown in our gardens. The root of lily-of-the-valley is especially poisonous. Several poppy relatives, such as opium poppy, Mexican poppy, celandine, and bloodroot contain powerful alkaloids.

Pasture weeds that kill or injure livestock are a problem to stockmen in all parts of the world. The several mountain laurels are among these. The common name for one species is "lambkill." Several species of larkspur or delphinium are bad offenders. A few of the more common poisonous pasture weeds in the United States are water hemlock, white snakeroot, death camas, spring rabbit brush, and loco weed. The word "loco" means "crazy" in Spanish, referring to the behavior of livestock poisoned by this plant. The leaves of the common chokecherry, especially when wilted, contain prussic acid and are poisonous to stock. Even the common black-eyed Susan is listed among the plants killing livestock.

Recently a new group of plants with peculiar toxic action has been investigated. They contain chemicals termed photodynamic. Livestock eating such plants may show no distress whatever. However, if the animal eats enough of the plant, and if the animal is white or has white spots on his body and, finally, if the animal is exposed to strong sunlight, the unpigmented areas sunburn severely and cause considerable trouble. Species of St. John's wort (Hypericum), buckwheat, and several others have been shown to cause photodynamic action. One of the worst of these is Klamath weed, native to Europe. This has run rampant over much of the western United States and parts of Australia, ruining thousands of acres of grazing or pasture land. An interesting method is being used to bring it under control. A beetle that lives on it has been introduced, and in the absence of hyperparasites[1], these are cutting down on the Klamath weed population. (Exactly the same method was used to get rid of prickly pear in Australia — see chapter on weeds.) Species of Hypericum are native to many parts of the country. Stockmen usually do not know the plant and are totally unaware of the damage it can do. I have encountered pastures yellow with its flowers in parts of Michigan, for example. I have also talked to stockmen in Michigan with stock injured by this plant and was able to enlighten them on the cause of the trouble.

Plants in several families found growing in the West may or

---

[1]Hyperparasites are parasites that live on a parasite, in this case, organisms that would attack the beetle.

may not contain poisons of their own, but they do have the property of absorbing compounds of selenium from the soil, which in turn poison stock. *Astragalus* and other legumes and several species in the Compositae (daisy relatives) are examples.

A few years ago I was called to examine a dairy farm in Delaware where there had been considerable trouble with aborted calves and unthrifty cows. The veterinarian in charge had obtained only negative results in tests for Bang's disease, also called contagious abortion, a bacterial infection. I went over the pasture with great care and found nothing except some bracken fern which, while poisonous, would not cause such symptoms. The pasture was rough with many stumps and boulders, and it had never been mowed. The veterinarian, the owner, and I sat down to talk it over, and finally I began to describe the several symptoms of ergot poisoning. When I mentioned that in addition to abortion, poisoned cows are prone to lose their tails, the farmer said, "That's it, all right". We began to reconstruct the history of the trouble. The spring that year had been warm and wet, a condition favorable for the development of ergot in the pasture grasses. With the pasture unmowed, the animals had eaten enough of the ergot to become poisoned. By the time I arrived the pasture grasses had shed their seeds, along with the resting or overwintering stage of the ergot, and no evidence remained.

Ergot is fungus, most commonly observed in the sclerotial or resting stage. This stage consists of cigar-shaped, purple-black, hard masses, which entirely replace some of the kernels in the heads of the infected grasses. In rye, for example, they are as shown in in Figure 37. If these sclerotia fall to the earth, the following spring

Figure 37

Ergot Sclerotia in Grass Head

each will form several small sporebearing structures. The spores are discharged forcibly and these infect grass flowers. As the flowers develop, there is formed a syruplike substance called "honey dew." This contains a second spore form of the fungus. Honey dew is carried from one grass flower to another by flies and other insects, and thus the infection is spread. Finally, as the seeds or kernels of the grains or other grasses mature, the resting or sclerotial stage of the ergot is formed, thus completing the cycle.

Certain of the ergot alkaloids have the effect of blocking off the smaller blood vessels of animals that have eaten ergot sclerotia. This results in a dry gangrene of extremities — hoofs, tails, ears or even limbs — which then slough off without bleeding. Abortion, as we have said, is another effect of ergot poisoning.

Ergot occurs in all of our common grains except corn and the sorghum group and on many uncultivated grasses. It is very prevalent in rye. During the Middle Ages the common people of Europe depended on rye for much of their bread. In years favorable to ergot the dread St. Anthony's Fire would ravage the land. The name St. Anthony's Fire is derived from a French saint of the eleventh century whose grave became a shrine of healing for the terrible scourge. However, in A.D. 954, if not earlier, the people learned that if they found refuge in the monasteries or churches, they were frequently cured. In that year there was a plague of ergot near Paris, and many of the afflicted fled to the Church of St. Mary in Paris. There they were fed with good bread made from flour from the ergot-free granaries of Duke Hugh the Great (father of Hugh Capet, who founded a French dynasty). The good bread of the monasteries, the churches, and the shrine of St. Anthony explains these miraculous cures. The true cause of ergot poisoning was not discovered until the eighteenth century.

The history of ergot poisoning is ancient. Assyrians recorded it as early as 600 B.C. There is no reason to doubt that this scourge is as old as the use of rye for human food — and for the grass-eating animals, even older. Even today it is still with us. In the autumn of 1951 four people were killed and forty sickened by ergot poisoning in the village of Pont-Saint Esprit in France.

The fact that the ergot sclerotia are larger than the kernels of grain makes their mechanical removal from grain a simple process. The ergot removed from the grain, because of its use in medicine, is worth far more than the grain. One use is to stop bleeding following childbirth. Certain of the ergot drugs are used to cure migraine headaches. Incidentally, Moorish physicians wrote of the use of ergot in childbirth around A.D. 1000, while Chinese midwives employed it even earlier.

This account would not be complete without mention of poisons in the trial and punishment of criminals. The American Indians used water hemlock[2] in the parsley family. In ancient Greece another "criminal," Socrates, was executed by means of the related poison hemlock. In many parts of the world the "ordeal" poisons have been long used. Among these poisons are *Physostigma*

---

[2]Not to be confused with the evergreen tree, *Tsuga canadensis,* known as "hemlock" in this country.

venenosum and *Erythrophleum guianensis,* both legumes and certain *Elaeodendron* species, related to our shrubby bittersweet. Their use is simplicity itself. A man is accused of a crime. He is made to drink a preparation of the poison. If he vomits and purges, he is innocent and will recover. Not many recover, and so most of those accused and thus tried are found guilty. The practice saves court costs.

FOR FURTHER READING

Creekmore, Hubert, *Daffodils are Dangerous: The Poisonous Plants in Your Garden;* Walker and Co., 1966.

Hill, A. F., *Economic Botany;* McGraw Hill Co., 1952.

Kingsbury, John M., *Deadly Harvest;* Holt, Rinehart, and Winston, 1965.

Muenscher, Waller C., *Poisonous Plants of the United States,* Revised Edition; The Macmillan Co., 1951.

FAMILIES OF PLANTS FOR GENERA IN THIS CHAPTER

Genera	Common Names	Families
Acokanthera spp.		Apocynaceae
Aconitum napellus	Monk's Head	Ranunculaceae
Amanita muscaria	Fly Agaric	Agaricaceae
Amanita phalloides	Death Angel	Agaricaceae
Amaryllis belladonna	Belladonna Lily	Amaryllidaceae
Antiaris toxicaria	Upas Tree	Moraceae
Areca Catechu	Betel Palm	Palmae
Argemone mexicana	Mexican Poppy	Papaveraceae
Astragalus mollissimus	Loco Weed	Leguminosae
Buphane disticha		Amaryllidaceae
Cannabis sativa	Marijuana, Hemp, Hashish	Cannabinaceae of some authorities; Moraceae of others
Cicuta spp.	Water Hemlock	Umbelliferae
Claviceps purpurea	Ergot	Hypocreaceae
Conium maculatum	Poison Hemlock	Umbelliferae
Convallaria majalis	Lily-of-the-Valley	Liliaceae
Datura spp.	Angel Trumpet, Jimson Weed, etc.	Solanaceae
Delphinium spp.	Larkspur	Ranunculaceae
Derris spp.	Derris	Leguminosae
Digitalis species, for example, D. *purpurea*	Foxglove	Scrophulariaceae
Erythroxylon coca	Cocaine Plant	Erythroxylaceae

Genera	Common Names	Families
Eupatorium rugosum	White Snakeroot	Compositae
Euphorbia spp.		Euphorbiaceae
Fagopyrum spp.	Buckwheat	Polygonaceae
Gluta renghas	Renghas	Anacardiaceae
Hippomane mancinella	Manchineel	Euphorbiaceae
Hymenocallis litteralis	Spider Lily	Amaryllidaceae
Hypericum perforatum,	Klamath Weed,	Hypericaceae
H. spp.	St. John's Wort	
Kalmia spp.	Mountain Laurels	Ericaceae
Lonchocarpus spp.		Leguminosae
Lophophora williamsii	Pellote, Peyote	Cactaceae
Lycoris radiata	Lycoris	Amaryllidaceae
Manihot utilissima	Cassava, Tapioca-	Euphorbiaceae
(*M. esculenta*)	Plant	
Metopium toxiferum	Poison Wood	Anacardiaceae
Narcissus poeticus	Narcissus	Amaryllidaceae
Narcissus Pseudo Narcissus	Daffodil	Amaryllidaceae
Papaver somniferum	Opium Poppy	Papaveraceae
Piptadenia peregrina	Cajobo (Că-hō-bō)	Leguminosae
Prunus virginiana	Chokecherry	Rosaceae
Rudbeckia spp.	Black-Eyed Susan	Compositae
Rhus radicans, Rhus	Poison Ivy and	Anacardiaceae
vernix, Rhus straita	Poison Sumac	
Sanguinaria canadensis	Bloodroot	Papaveraceae
Scilla spp.	Squill	Amaryllidaceae
Strophanthus spp.		Apocynaceae
Strychnos spp.	Strychnine, Curare	Loganiaceae
Tephrosia spp.		Leguminosae
Tetradymia glabrata	Spring Rabbit Brush	Compositae
Zephyranthus atamasco	Atamasco Lily	Amaryllidaceae
Zygdenus spp.	Death Camas	Liliaceae

CHAPTER 12

What the Doctor Prescribed

RIMITIVE man was even more subject to diseases, aches, pains, and wounds than we are today. Even as we do, he tried to cure himself. Doubtless most of his experiments in medication were failures. Usually he got well anyway — in spite of his medicines. However, once in a while something worked. If, through the ages, almost every available material is tried for almost every conceivable application, a number of useful combinations are inevitable.

Most of the remedies derived from plants were known to the common people, or to the would-be healers among them, long before they were accepted into recognized medical practice. Of course, much that was used by laymen, by witch doctors, and by physicians up to recent times was worthless or even injurious. The administration of remedies among primitive peoples was often combined with superstition and ritual, all of which does not change the fact that primitive peoples have made many valuable medical discoveries.

If you work among the people of the jungle, you soon come to realize that the more intelligent natives are apt to be good natural botanists. They will, of course, know nothing of scientific terminology, but they will know plants. They have common names for each and know their uses, including medicinal uses.

One of the most historically famous examples is the use of the bark of species of *Cinchona* in the treatment of malaria. The word "malaria" means "bad air." The disease was so named because it is most prevalent in low, hot, swampy places where mosquitoes carrying the disease organism are abundant.

The first knowledge to reach Europe concerning the wonderful bark that is the source of quinine supposedly came about somewhat as follows: When Phillip became King of Spain in 1628 he appointed Don Luis Geronimo Fernandez Cabrera Bobadilla y Mendoz (whose titles included that of Conde de Cinchon), viceroy over all of the New World at that time claimed by Spain. The seat of Spanish government in the New World was Lima, Peru, and to that settlement Don Luis took his bride. According to the story, she became desperately ill with malaria a few years later. Near death, she was brought back to health by an infusion of "quina quina" bark, sent to her physician by Don Juan Lopez de Canizares, the magistrate of Loxa, in the interior. Don Juan had himself been cured of malaria by use of the bark. After her recovery the condesa refused to remain in the colonies and embarked for Spain, taking with her a shipment of Cinchona bark. It is known that she died at sea early in the voyage and was buried in or near Colombia. It is claimed that the "quina quina" bark went on to Spain.

Recent perusal of private papers of this family in Spain have cast some doubt upon the story. Records are fairly clear, however, that Don Juan Lopez de Canizares was probably the first white man known to history to have been cured of malaria by the use of the "quina quina" bark. However, the supposed connection of the plant with the Conde de Cinchon is perpetuated in the generic name, *Cinchona,* applied to the trees from which the bark is obtained. *Cinchona* belongs in the same plant family as coffee[1]. Several species of *Cinchona* contain sufficient quinine to be of value, while others are relatively useless.

Among the first advocates of the use of *Cinchona* bark were the Jesuit missionaries, and the name "Jesuits' powder" still clings to it. The association of the Jesuits with the Peruvian bark had its drawbacks, however, because it was rumored among Protestants that Jesuit's powder was a dangerous poison, part of a supposed plot by the pope to poison Protestants in wholesale lots.

The acceptance of the miraculous bark into medical use in Europe was further hampered by certain unpleasant effects connected with its administration, poor results with adulterated or ineffective material, the practices of charlatans, the stiff conservatism of many of the medical authorities of the period, and the high price the Spanish monopoly was able to maintain. However, the use of the bark was bound to spread since very probably malaria was the most important killer in the world at that time. Even today it is estimated that around 800,000,000 people almost constantly suffer from malaria.

---

[1]A list of plant families for the several genera is appended at the end of the chapter.

As the use of Peruvian bark became more widespread, the traffic in it became increasingly lucrative. Spanish efforts to maintain monoply of the trade were only exceeded by the determination of other nations to break that monopoly. The Dutch sent a Dr. Hasskarl into the area to bring out viable *Cinchona* material, while Ledger, Markham, and Spruce made separate similar attempts for the British. The stories of their adventures[2] are hair-raising. These men were in constant danger of being killed by the Spanish or by the natives, as well as by diseases and other mishaps. While all of these men finally succeeded in obtaining and bringing out viable matrial, the Dutch were the most successful in growing *Cinchona* in the Dutch East Indies, where they established thriving plantations run in a scientific and efficient manner. They were even able to produce several *Cinchona* hybrids with quinine content far higher than that occurring in trees found in nature. At present, synthetic drugs, many of them related to quinine in structure, are coming into extensive use in combating malaria. Atabrin and plasmoquine are examples. These drugs are designed to do the work of quinine without quinine's undesirable side effects.

The cocaine and opium alkaloids, which helped to open the paths to modern anesthesia in dentistry, surgery, and general medicine, had long been used by the peoples of South America and Asia respectively before they came to the attention of medical science. The cocaine alkaloids are obtained from the leaves of the shrub *Erythroxylon coca.* Opium is obtained from scarified seed capsules of the opium poppy, *Papaver somniferum.* This is not the flaming Oriental poppy of our gardens, which is *Papaver orientale,* but a species with flowers variously colored white, purple or red.

The introduction of these drugs into our pharmacology was not an unmixed blessing. Physicians had to learn the hard way that these pain killers are addictive drugs, capable of doing great harm. Only since the advent of the Federal Harrison Narcotics Act in 1914 (and similar legislation in other countries) has the flagrant abuse of these drugs been made illegal.

Chaulmoogra oil has been used "since time immemorial" in India for the treatment of leprosy. This oil is obtained from the seeds of *Hydnocarpus wrightiana, H. anthelmintiea, Taraktogenos kurzii,* and other species. Chaulmoogra oil contains chemicals highly lethal to the bacterium that causes leprosy. Its use, however, causes considerable pain, and there is a tendency among patients to won-

---

[2]The story is well told in *Cargoes and Harvests* by Donald Culross Peattie.

der whether the treatment is not worse than the disease. Only recently has science been able to separate the effective components from those that make its use painful.

Medical science picked up ipecac from the South American Indians, and this drug is still very much in the pharmacopoeia of modern medicine. It is obtained from *Cephaelis ipecacuanha* and other species in Brazil. Ipecac is a safe alkaloid emetic when correctly administered. In small amounts it stimulates the appetite and aids digestion.

For years doctors argued over the reported value of ipecac in control of dysentery, some reporting wonderful cures and others total failure. Only when science came to recognize the existence of causal organisms could the truth be found. Ipecac kills entamabae, which cause amebic dysentery, at one part in ten thousand, but is utterly worthless as a bactericide and it will not control bacterial dysenteries. At present emetine hydrochloride, a salt of the emetic principle of ipecac, is the form most commonly employed in medicine.

In Europe the common people had long used digitalis or foxglove (*Digitalis purpurea*) for treatment of dropsy, which is caused by weak heart action. The most evident symptom of this disease is a swelling of the body, often starting at the joints but eventually extending to all parts, as a result of accumulation of serum in the body tissues. The name "dropsy" is derived from "hydrops," a Greek word meaning "water disease."

Digitalis was only admitted to general medical use after many false starts. It contains several powerful toxic glucosides and these, if improperly administered, can be extremely harmful or even fatal. Different people show totally different reactions to the drug. A dose that would be dangerous for one patient may be less than effective for another. Not until doctors began to recognize the special nature of the drug could it come into general use. An overdose causes the heart to beat with powerful, slow strokes, as though it would explode the chest, and produces a feeling of terror. (I know this by experience.) Some patients are made to vomit and purge by it. Properly used, however, digitalis is a valuable tool against dropsy.

While Europeans had been learning about digitalis, the American Indians had been treating dropsy with the unrelated plant, dogbane (*Apocynum cannabinum*), with similar results. Dogbane contains drugs that act similarly to those that occur in digitalis. Although still retained in *United States Dispensatory*[3], it is a less valuable drug than digitalis. The Indians of the American southwest used leaves of a cottonwood tree for the same purpose. In North Africa and other parts of the Mediterranean region squill (*Scilla* spp) and oleander (*Nerium Oleander*) have also been used in treating dropsy. Even in the absence of communication, various peoples had, through experimentation, learned many similar means of treating the same disease. A large group of the most powerful arrow poisons have been found to be effective in the treatment of dropsy when administered with care. Modern science discovered the use of the arrow poisons, but primitive trial and error discovered the rest.

In China several *Ephedra* species have been used in medicine "for thousands of years." Ephedrine, the active principle, is still one of the most valuable drugs in our modern pharmacopoeia. It is applied to the mucus membranes for treatment of colds. There are Ephedra species common to the desert areas of the southwestern United States, but these (in California, at least) do not appear to contain ephedrine. The drug, called *ma huang* by the Chinese, has the effect of shrinking mucus membranes, thus making breathing easier and relieving allergic reactions, such as hay fever. The Asiatics also introduced into medicine cubeb (*Piper Cubeba*). Cubeb cigarettes were once in very common use to shrink mucus membranes of the nasal cavity, thus relieving cold symptoms.

Cassia and senna (leaves of *Cassia* species) have long been used as laxatives in the Mediterranean area and neighboring regions. The cascara sagrada, one of the buckthorns (*Rhamnus purshiana*), used as a laxative by the Indians in northern California, is still widely used.

Atropine, obtained from *Atropa Belladonna,* is used by oculists to enlarge the pupil of the eye prior to examination.[4] Belladonna means "beautiful woman" in Italian. This name originated through the use of the plant by ladies in Italy at one time to make their eyes lustrous and mysterious. During World War II supplies of atropine became scarce, and the drug was obtained from leaves of the related *Datura Stramonium*. Both plants are relatives of potato and tomato. Both are extremely poisonous and so are several related species, for example, the deadly nightshade. The slow course of the toxic action of belladonna and the uncertainty of its symptoms

[3]The standard reference book of drug materials.
[4]Atropine, properly used, is an excellent anti-spasmodic for severe asthma.

made it a favorite with professional poisoners during the Middle Ages. It has been used (along with *Datura* species) to poison people in India since ancient times. The red berries of *Atropa* species are attractive to children and have resulted in poisoning.

Many plants have been in use for a long time to control intestinal parasites. American wormseed (*Chenopodium ambrosioides*), related to beets and spinach, is a fairly common weed in many parts of the United States. It is a rank-smelling plant, and from it is obtained an oil that is very effective against hookworms, round worms, and amebic dysentery. Male fern (*Aspidium* sp.) has been used to kill tapeworm since the days of Pliny the Elder, about the time of Christ, and is still so used. In fact, it is still considered one of the best drugs for this purpose.

There are a great many more of these ancient plant drugs that are still in more or less common use in medicine. Only in comparatively recent times have two new groups of medicinals derived from plants come into common use. These are the several vitamins and the antibiotics. It was pointed out in the chapter on fruits that many of them are sources of vitamin C, the preventive and cure for scurvy. When the East India Company provided limes or other citrus for their sailors in 1601, they made medical history and at the same time fastened the names "limeys" and limejuicers" on British mariners and ships respectively, which names persist today. Vitamin A occurs in carrots and other vegetables. Lack of sufficient amounts of vitamin A results in night blindness, digestive troubles, and other unpleasant disorders. Vitamin B, found in the coats of grain seeds and in other plant parts, must be sufficient in the diet or the disease called beri beri results. Frankly, people eating a good, mixed diet and getting sufficient sunlight probably have little chance of vitamin deficiency, but human diets being what they often are, such deficiencies can and do occur.

The antibiotics came into the medical picture when A. Fleming noticed in 1929 that cultures of the fungus *Penicillium notatum* inhibited growth of bacteria. We have discussed these chemical defense mechanisms of plants in Chapter 4. It just so happens that the active principle employed by this fungus is tolerated fairly well by man and other warm-blooded animals, and this fact opened up many new approaches to disease control. Since that time several other valuable antibiotic substances have been introduced into therapeutic use. These include tyrothricin, secreted by a soil bacterium; *Bacillus brevis*, clavicin, obtained from *Aspergillus clavatus, Penicillium claviforme* and *P. patulum;* bacitracin, a product of

Bacillus subtilis; and others. There is every reason to believe that the search for antibiotics will continue for years and will result in many valuable discoveries.

A discussion of plants in relation to medicine would not be complete without a few words on the doctrine of signatures. It seems that shapes of plants and plant parts have suggested medicinal uses to primitive man and to later practitioners of the healing arts. In the sixteenth century this idea was given the formal blessing of Philippus Aureolus Theophrastus Bombastus Paracelsus von Hohenheim, who advanced the theory that the Diety had placed His seal on all things of possible use in medicine. Thus, the three-lobed, liver-colored (on the under side) leaves of liverwort must be good for afflictions of the liver. Bloodroot would be beneficial in diseases involving the blood. Much-branched plants would obviously be of use in bronchial troubles, while heart-shaped leaves were plainly meant to be used for heart troubles. Leaves that trembled, as in the aspen, should be useful in treatment of palsy. Believe it or not, since lunatics are supposed to be moonstruck — hence the name — and because silver has been associated in the popular mind with the moon[5], silver preparations were used to treat insanity. Fortunately, saner counsel took over, and the doctrine of signatures passed into oblivion, at least among the more civilized peoples.

There have been many volumes written on the subject of plants in relation to medicine. For those who wish to read further, here are a few references:

Clymen, M. D., and R. Swinburne, *Nature's Healing Agents;* Donance, 1963.

Coon, Nelson, *Using Plants for Healing;* Hearthside.

Corlett, W. T., *The Medicine Man of the American Indians;* Charles C. Thomas, Springfield, Illinois, 1935.

Kreig, Margaret B., *Green Medicine;* Rand Mc Nally, 1964.

Silverman, Milton, *Magic in a Bottle;* The Macmillan Company, New York, 1944.

Sollman, T., *A Manual of Pharmacology;* W. B. Saunders Co., Philadelphia, Pa.

United States Dispensatory; The J. B. Lippincott Co., Philadelphia, Pa.

Taylor, Norman, *Plant Drugs that Changed the World;* Dodd, 1965.

PLANT FAMILIES FOR GENERA IN THIS CHAPTER

Scientific Name	Common Name	Family
Apocynum cannabinum	Dogbane	Apocynaceae

[5]The common name for silver nitrate is lunar caustic.

Scientific Name	Common Name	Family
Atropa Belladonna	Belladonna	Solanaceae
Cassia species	Cassia, Senna	Leguminceae
Cephaelis ipecacuanha	Ipecac	Rubiaceae
Chenopodium ambrosioides	American Wormseed	Chenopodiaceae
Cinchona spp.	Quinine Tree	Rubiaceae
Datura Stramonium	Jimson Weed	Solanaceae
Digitalis purpurea	Foxglove	Scrophulariaceae
Ephedra species	Ma Huang, etc.	Gnetaceae
Erythroxylon coca	Cocaine Plant	Erythroxylaceae
Hydnocarpus species		Flacourtiaceae
Nerium Oleander	Oleander	Apocynaceae
Papaver somniferum	Opium Poppy	Papaveraceae
Piper Cubeba	Cubeb	Piperaceae
Rhamnus purshiana	Cascara	Rhamnaceae
Scilla species	Squill	Liliaceae
Taraktogenos kurzii		Flacourtiaceae

CHAPTER 13

The Ancestors

PLANTS have existed on this earth for a long time. There are well-preserved fossil algae (ancestors of our present day seaweeds and pond scums) and fungi from around two billion years[1] back. Plants change as the centuries roll by. Few, if any, plant species of ten million years ago would have remained constant enough through the ages to be assigned to the same species today. It is probable that evolutionary changes in less than a million years would necessitate reclassification of many plants. By the end of that time a species might have changed into one or several new species, or have become extinct. On earth at present there are probably over 250,000 named and described plant species. It is obvious that there must have been a vastly greater number through past ages. If we consider the haphazard manner in which plant material from past ages has been preserved, we will have some idea of the magnitude of the task that faces paleobotanists (scientists who study ancient plants).

How is plant material preserved? There are several ways. Re-

---

[1]These time periods are, of course, estimates. There are several ways by which such estimates may be made. For example, living plants contain a constant amount of radio-active carbon. After plants have died, the radio-active carbon breaks down at a predictable rate permitting determination of age of the material.

If we can associate uranium ore with a particular geological formation, we have another means of dating because uranium breaks down to form lead according to the formula:

$$\text{Years elapsed} = 1.5 \times 10^{10} \log 10 \frac{(U + Pb)}{(U)}$$

which means that if we add the weight of the uranium and lead in the ore, and then divide this by the weight of the uranium, then take the logarithm of the quotient to the base 10 and multiply this by 1.5×10^{10}, we have the age of the ore specimen, and from this the age of the geological formation in which it occurs. This latter method, where it can be used, is especially valuable for dating very ancient deposits.

cently I examined a huge floating platform used in connection with the sinking of oil wells in Lake Maracaibo, South America. The frame of the platform was constructed of great steel tubes, some of them vertical, some horizontal. The twenty-five foot vertical tubes were badly rusted near the water surface, becoming less so in increasing depths until, at the bottom, the low oxygen concentration kept them practically free of rust.

For steel to rust, or for plants to decay, oxygen is required. If leaves, branches, seeds, or pollen grains are buried in mud, earth, water, or volcanic ash rapidly and deeply enough to cut off the supply of oxygen, the fungi and bacteria responsible for decay will not be able to do their work, and the plant tissues, more or less modified by their physical surroundings, will be fossilized. Obviously, the weight of soil on these plant materials will usually flatten them out to a greater or less extent, hence the term "compression fossils." Occasionally volcanic ash will cover whole forests and preserve the less destructible tissues. In one location in the western United States there are seventeen such buried forests, one above the other.

Impression fossils are merely imprints of leaves or other plant parts on mud which has later turned to rock. Many of these are beautifully clear, showing patterns of bark or other plant parts. While they are of considerable value in studying gross structures, examination of tissues with a microscope is, obviously, impossible in impression fossils.

What happens to the plant material once it is buried will depend on the physical and chemical conditions that follow. Tissues encased in shale or limestone usually retain some of the carbon of the original tissues. If the fossil material is impregnated with silica, this may, and usually does, entirely replace the carbon of the tissues, resulting in complete petrifaction, although the pattern of the tissues may be beautifully preserved.

Certain plant tissues, because of their composition or structure, are more likely to be preserved than others. Heavy, leathery leaves, for example, would be more apt to be preserved than thin, fragile ones. The pollen grains of wind-pollinated plants and the spores of plants reproducing by means of spores, such as ferns, equisetum relatives, mosses and club mosses, are produced in enormous numbers (and are often provided with a resistant cuticle). These will be carried by wind and streams to bogs and lakes. There they will be covered with mud and water and become preserved, while the vastly larger plants that produced them will mature, die, and decay, and only under the most favorable circumstances be preserved. This will be especially true of herbaceous plants.

Certain very important groups of plants, for example, bacteria, many of the algae, and practically all of the fungi or molds, are rather infrequently found preserved because the very soft nature of their tissues usually permits them to decay rapidly or to be crushed beyond recognition. However, the brackets formed on tree trunks by certain fungi (conks or punks), for example, those in genus *Polyporus*[2], are quite woody and are often found in fossil state. Fungi send threads called hyphae through the tissues of the plant on which they are parasitic. These hyphae correspond roughly to the roots and stems of higher plants as far as their functions are concerned. Hyphae of fungi attacking wood are found rather frequently in sections of prehistoric wood.

The algae, except for the silica shells of the diatoms, are preserved only, as a rule, when they have been mineralized rather rapidly. We may infer the presence of algae in the past by the character of certain limestone deposits. However, a few beautifully preserved alga and fungus specimens have been found.

How does the paleobotanist go about examining fossil plant remains? Some of these remains are so little mineralized that they may be impregnated with plastic materials and sectioned[3] directly for examination under the microscope. If the plant tissues have become mineralized, the mineral may in some cases be removed by treatment with chemicals.

The peel technique is widely used for specimens encased in rock — usually calcium carbonate. The rock is cut and polished to reveal the structures to be examined. If the rock is calcium carbonate, the surface is treated with dilute hydrochloric acid. This treatment dissolves a thin layer of the rock, but does not attack the carbon residues of the plant tissues. The surface is then carefully washed, dried, and sprayed with cellulose acetate in suitable solvent, usually amyl acetate (the mixture is much akin to that used for fingernail polish). The resulting films, when dry, are then peeled off. The carbon structures are beautifully preserved in the transparent films, and may be examined under the microscope, photographed, and filed for future reference.

---

[2]See chapter on fungi.

[3]Sectioning is usually done with a microtome, a mechanical device that slices off thin pieces of known thickness. These slices, after appropriate further treatment, may be mounted on glass slides for examination under the microscope.

If the plant structures have been completly replaced by mineral, usually silica, as in petrified wood, thin sections may be cut and polished for examination under the microscope.

Pollen grains and spores in soft coal may be separated out in a few days by treatment of crumbs of coal with a mixture of potassium chlorate and concentrated nitric acid. (Careful — this mixture is "strong medicine".) After the coal has been thus treated, the residue is washed several times in water and finally treated with dilute ammonia for a few hours. If the structures to be examined are still badly flattened, they may be plumped up by heating for a few hours with alcoholic potassium hydroxide. Tissues found in lignite, a material intermediate between peat and coal, are usually in better condition than those in soft coal. In anthracite (hard) coal the plant residues are usually too far altered to be of much value to the paleobotanist.

By comparing the gross and microscopic structures of modern and ancient plants, and by determining the ages of the fossils collected from different regions, it is possible to gain some idea of what kind of plants lived where in what ages. Because of the chance manner in which plant material is preserved, however, plant structures are often found associated with structures of totally unrelated plants which may have grown originally in different habitats and often in locations miles apart. Because of this, much study and sorting is necessary before it can be decided what structures are properly associated with what ancient plant.

Occasionally the paleobotanist is helped in his work by the findings of scientists in other fields. The paleozoologists (students of fossil animal forms), for example, discovered that a considerable increase in the height of crowns of teeth occurred in herbivorous animals during the Miocene (about ten million years ago) period. From the standpoint of the long periods of time usually involved, the change came about in a relatively short time, as though natural selection had been given a powerful impetus. This would indicate a diet of tougher plants than had previously been eaten. The Miocene period marked the spread of prairies, with the tough prairie grasses.

Present-day plant species may be confined to a particular climatic zone, but it does not necessarily follow that all of the ancestors or ancient relatives demanded the same conditions. When we find fossil cycads[4] in Greenland, for example, the question arises, Was

---

[4]The featherlike cycad fronds are sometimes used for "palm" branches on Palm Sunday. They are not palms.

Greenland once tropical, or were cycads growing there capable of thriving under temperate conditions? Additional evidence has indicated that not only Greenland, but also Alaska was at one time semitropical. On the other hand, fossil remains of spruce forests in Piedmont district of South Carolina would indicate that that region was once much cooler. Vast coal deposits formed under conditions of lush tropical growth are found in regions that are now arid or even deserts.

Like many other sciences, paleobotany and its sister science, paleozoology, have had a rather irregular growth. Xanthus, about 500 B.C., observed fossil shells in rocks in Phrygia and Lydia, far from the sea, and surmised that the area was once covered by the ocean. Herodotus, about 484 B.C., drew a parallel conclusion when he observed sea shells in the Libyan desert near the Oasis of Ammon. Theophrastus (368-284 B.C.) wrote a treatise on fossils. The manuscript has been lost, but Pliny quotes it repeatedly. Centuries later, Leonardo da Vinci, who was a pioneer in many things, from aviation to anatomy, wrote understandingly of the nature of fossils.

However, as recently as two hundred years ago there were men who called themselves scientists, men supposedly able and well trained, who believed that all fossils were mere freaks of nature, with no connection with plants or animals once living, to say nothing of present-day plants and animals.

Paleobotany and paleozoology, as modern sciences, got off to a slow but steady and more organized start at the beginning of the eighteenth century and, until quite recently, have been advanced largely by the work of a few great and devoted men. The obvious vastness of the work leaves the fields of these two sciences wide open to students and research workers for many years to come.

Where, in the United States, would a person be able to find fossil plant material? As we said before, soft coal and lignite, if properly handled, will reveal much ancient plant material still capable of study. The mud of lake beds or bogs contains diatoms, pollen grains, and other remnants.

Here is a list of some of the localities in the United States where fossil plant remains may be found.

Location	Materials	Remarks
Florissant, Colorado, and Yellowstone National Park, Arizona	Petrified forests	In successive ages, forests grew, and then were covered with earth and volcanic ash.

Location	*Materials*	*Remarks*
Petrified Forest National Park, Arizona	Petrified forests	
Near Wayan, Idaho	Tree fern stumps genus *Tempskya*	Petrified
South of Kemmerer, Wyoming	Ferns	These are well preserved in white shales.
Gros Ventre Canyon, Western Wyoming	Araucarian[5] wood	
Lompoc, California (and elsewhere)	Diatomaceous earth	This is a huge deposit of the microscopic silica cases of diatoms.
Sodon Lake district, Oakland County, Mich.	Pollen deposits	These are found in ancient lakes or bogs.
Goshen, west central Oregon	Fossilized plants	Type of flora indicates warmer conditions prevailing when these deposits were laid down.
New Jersey, clay deposits in several areas	Logs, branches, cones, and araucarian wood	These are in remarkable state of preservation; can be sectioned with a microtome, after imbedding in plastic, for examination under the microscope.
Iowa and Illinois	Coal balls	These structures, found in coal measures, are usually silicified, with all of the original carbon replaced.
Kettle Point, Ontario, Canada (near Sarnia, on Lake Ontario)[6]	Petrified woods, including gymnosperm types (pine relatives)	Specimens scattered in "kettles" on a rocky beach.
Will County, Illinois	Mazon Creek nodules with leaves of Pteridosperms	The plant structures were originally encased in mud which

[5]Araucaria is a genus in Pinaceae, at one time very widespread, but now restricted to widely separated areas and extinct in the northern hemisphere. There are *Araucarias* flourishing today as part of the flora of South America; and one of them, *Araucaria excelsa,* the beautiful Norfolk Island pine is commonly planted in warmer parts of the United States.

[6]There are also deposits containing countless brachiopod shells at Kettle Point. These clam-like shells are in a beautiful state of preservation. I have collected quarts of them.

	(these are pine relatives)	has now changed to rock. The nodules are oblong in shape.
Grand Ledge, ten miles west of Lansing, Mich.	Carboniferous age[7] compressions	These are associated with thin coal seams.
The Catskills, New York State	Material from the Devonian[8] period, including pine relatives and spore-bearing plants.	

The layers of earth immediately above coal beds and black shales are usually good sources of fossil plant material. Fossil deposits in the eastern United States are usually quite ancient. Those of the West are usually comparatively recent. The best states for fossil hunting in the East include Pennsylvania, New York, Virginia, West Virginia, Iowa, and Michigan. In the West, Arizona and Wyoming are sources of much fossil material.

One of the most fascinating studies connected with paleobotany is that of phylogeny. That is, what ancient plants were related to what present-day plants? How and why did the different plants evolve as they did? Do all land plants stem from one common ancestor that left the water to become a land dweller, or were there several advances from the sea to the land, giving rise early to widely differing groups?

The earliest land plants found as fossils are generally fairly well advanced. This is just what we would expect. Chance preservation of plant tissues would mean that the rarer earlier forms, those we might call the pioneers, would be much less frequently encountered than their well-adapted and widely distributed descendants. Further, the first plants to emerge from the sea would doubtless be less woody than their descendants, and would thus be less apt to be preserved. There were probably many advances from the sea that eventually came to an end, with the extinction of entire groups, possibly in some cases after a period of initial success. The great group called the Nematophytales, for example, was widespread during the Silurian period and through the Devonian period, dying out completely early in the Mississippian or Lower Carboniferous period.[9]

---

[7]Around 223 million years ago.
[8]309-354 million years ago.
[9]Around 250 million years ago.

Living creatures span their cycles and reproduce in relation to other living creatures and to physical environment. Sometimes two different organisms may be in competition, occasionally so intense that one or both may become greatly modified, or even extinct. Physical environment is prone to change, slowly or suddenly, necessitating adaptation to survive. If succeeding generations of plants or animals change rapidly enough to keep abreast or ahead of the needs of the moment, no more is required of them for survival. The time element is especially important when we consider how vast the periods are that have elapsed since life began on this planet — time enough for high mountains to be worn down to smooth plains!

To exist at all, an organism must be able to nourish itself, absorbing or manufacturing the compounds, living or inanimate, of which it is composed. To do this requires energy, derived originally from the sun and, in secondary systems, by the oxidative process called respiration. Waste products must be eliminated. The necessary responses of the moment to physical, and often biological, environment must be provided for, and some method of reproduction will be necessary. With one-celled organisms these few processes are complex, but with the larger organisms (those that are adapted to more complex surroundings) multiple structures and functions of even greater complexity are necessary.

If I say, "This is a frog. It lives part of its life in water, part on land. It catches insects or other creatures for food. It may itself be caught by other animals for food," I have, in effect, said much more. I have said that this creature must have a means of moving about. This implies, in a creature as large as the frog, a muscular system. A muscular system, to function, must have some mechanism to direct and control it — the nervous system in this case. There must be a framework to which the muscles are attached — the skeleton. The muscles must receive nourishment in some manner, and likewise oxygen, to carry on the transformation of the stored energy of food to the kinetic energy of motion, in this case through the blood circulatory system. The frog must have a way of absorbing oxygen. The fact that, having no diaphragm, he must "swallow" air, or that in the tadpole stage he has gills and that throughout his life he absorbs much oxygen through his skin, makes no difference as long as he procures sufficient oxygen for his needs. The frog must have a means of detecting his food and also his enemies. For this the eyes are important. They may not be the same eyes as those of the crayfish, octopus, insect, or snail, but they must be sufficient for his mode of life. He must have some means of eliminating wastes from the body. The fact that his kidneys are located low in the abdomen, while those of the crayfish are located practically in the head, need not prevent either from succeeding in their modes of life. Thus we see that if an organism lives in a certain way, it must have whatever equipment is necessary to enable it to live in that way.

However, if two organisms have many points in common in their mode of life, this does not mean that their structures and processes are evolved from the same ancestor. Many structures have evolved many times, quite independently. For example, the eye evolved once in the vertebrates — fish, reptiles, birds, amphibians, and mammals. It evolved at least once in the mollusks — the squid and octopus are examples. Whether the eyes of the snails represent a separate evolution would have to be answered by the zoologists. Two distinct types of eyes, simple and compound, were evolved in the arthropods — the insects, spiders, crayfish, centipedes, and millepedes. Many totally unrelated creatures, such as the star fish and several worms, have light-sensitive spots which serve in part the function of an eye. These eyes and eye spots are not always strictly comparable in structure, but they serve very similar purposes.

An organism cannot fit into an environment or mode of life for which that organism has not yet evolved sufficiently effective structures. Any slight improvement of structure in relation to function will enable the organism to fit more successfully into its mode of life — or possibly into a more complex and advantageous one.

The same ideas are applicable to plants. The fact that two plants have leaves, trunks, seeds, roots, spines, or flowers, does not mean that these necessarily have descended from a common ancestor. Stems are useful structures on which to drape the flowers or other reproductive parts, to spread food-producing structures (leaves) in the air and light, and for other purposes. Leaves, because of their shapes, are able to catch more sunlight and air than stem structures and thus are more effective in food-production. On the other hand, they permit evaporation of much water, which may be a limiting factor in certain environments. It is possible that seeds have resulted from four or more separate lines of evolution. Spines and thorns for protection have evolved dozens of times. Totally unrelated plants, growing under like conditions, may grow to resemble each other closely.

Some of our present-day plants are but little different from their ancestors of several million years past. The ginkgo flourished widely, in much the same form as today, back 150 million years ago in Jurassic times, and over much of the world. Several species were native to our continent. Today there remains only one species, *Ginkgo biloba*. The fact that it has for centuries been a cultivated tree of Chinese gardens may be the only thing that saved it from extinction.

Figure 38

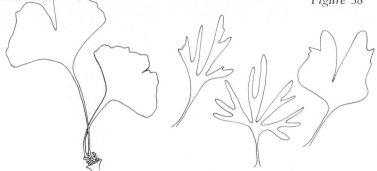

Present-day Gingko Foliage and Some Ancestral Forms

In 1941 fossils of *Metasequoia*, which has been given the common name "dawn redwood," an ancient form related to our redwoods, were found in Montana. Fossils were later encountered in Japan and China and all around the northern hemisphere. Then, about 1947 or 1948, it was found that *Metasequoia* was still very much alive in Szechuan Province in Central China. Although a number of trees were found, the species was of limited distribution

Figure 39

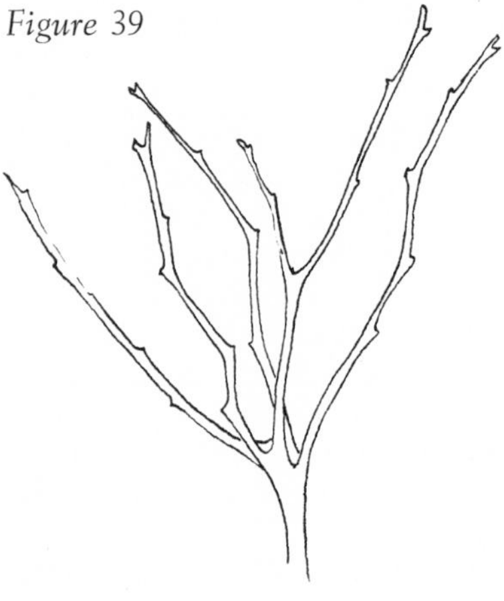

Stem or Branch of Whisk Fern

Figure 40

Restoration of Eospermatopteris, a Primitive Seed Fern (From: Arnold, An Introduction to Paleobotany, Courtesy: McGraw-Hill Book Co.)

and may have been heading for extinction. Now seeds have been sown in botanical gardens in many parts of the world.

Extremely primitive, but still persisting, is the little *Psilotum nudum* (whisk fern) of the tropics, a plant whose ancestors trace back to the Devonian period, about 350 million years ago. This little plant has never developed true leaves or roots at all.

The horse tail and scouring rush group (*Equisteum* spp.) is still relatively primitive in structure. The alga group is still very much a part of our modern flora, some forms possibly only slightly changed in four hundred million years or more.

In the Mid-Devonian period our country supported great forests of the primitive *Eospermatopteris,* a tree with fernlike foliage and trunks to three and a half feet in diameter. Later, in the Carboniferous ages (223 to 309 million years ago) there were great forests of tree ferns in the genus *Psæronius* with trunks to two feet in diameter. Once club moss relatives (*Lepidodendron* species)

Bark of a Lepidodendron, Natural Size *(From: Arnold, An Introduction to Paleobotany, Courtesy: McGraw-Hill Book Co.)*

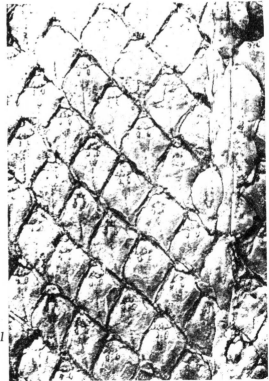

Figure 41

called giant club mosses, a hundred feet or more in height, with trunks two feet through, covered much of our country, and now all of these last three are extinct.

Specialized texts are available for more detailed study of this fascinating subject. Here are a few of them:

Andrews, Henry N., Jr., *Ancient Plants and the World They Lived In;* Comstock Publishing Co., Inc., Ithaca, New York, 1947. (Semipopular.)

Arnold, Chester A., *An Introduction to Paleobotany;* McGraw-Hill Book Co., New York, N. Y., 1947.

Arnold, Chester A., *Fossil Plants;* Houghton-Mifflin, 1968.

Seward, Albert C., *Links With the Past in the Plant World;* Stechert.

Seward, Albert C., *Plant Life Through the Ages;* Cambridge University Press, Cambridge, England, 1931, Revised 1959 (Hafner).

Walton, John, Jr., *An Introduction to the Study of Fossil Plants* (Second Edition); A. and C. Black, London, 1953. (Good brief account.)

There are also careful treatments of the subject in:

Botany: Wilson and Loomis; The Dryden Press, Inc., New York, 1957.

College Botany: Fuller and Tippo; Henry Holt and Co., New York, 1954.

In 1952, *Life* magazine published an excellent series entitled "The World We Live In" which contains a good resumé of paleobotany.

CHAPTER 14

Plants We Don't Like

OMING as I did from a family of gardeners, I had an early and always unpleasant acquaintance with weeds.* I can recall my father's dictum, "If you planted your garden on the moon, you'd still have weeds."

I remember the sandy playground around our school. Each fall we would return to find the whole schoolyard covered with sand-

Figure 42

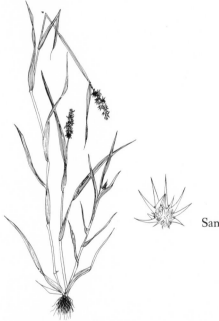

Sandbur

---

*Many of the illustrations in this chapter have been supplied through the kind cooperation of the Iowa Department of Agriculture.

burs. In those days bare feet were not at all uncommon, and crossing a field of sandburs barefooted was an adventure for martyrs.

Another grass, bristly foxtail (*Setaria verticillata*), is a miserable inhabitant of many fields, gardens, and orchards. The bristly heads cling to almost anything they touch. It is the bane of hunters, field or orchard workers, hunting dogs, and all animals that come in contact with it. I have seen grasshoppers an inch long caught and dead on the bristly heads, and once I freed a sparrow hawk that had apparently gotten his wings entangled as he dove down after a mouse. I have no idea how long he had been there, but he was very thin when I released him and there wasn't much fight left in him. The clinging bristles, of course, are the means employed by bristly foxtail to spread its seeds far and wide.

Have you ever seen puncture vine? It has yellow flowers and indented leaves, both suggestive of watermelon but in miniature. It spreads over the ground in a matlike growth. A vigorous plant may cover an area five feet or more in diameter. Each seed cluster is well armed with sharp thorns that may be a half inch in length. Supposedly it was named puncture vine because the thorns could pierce the old-fashioned high-pressure, thin-walled, auto tires. I can vouch for the fact that it can puncture human skin. The scientific name for this annual, *Tribulus terrestris,* means roughly "tribulation of the earth," which is appropriate.

Figure 43

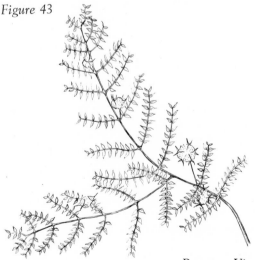

Puncture Vine (*Tribulus terrestris*)

Horse nettle or bull nettle is not a nettle at all, but a relative of potato. It is a perennial herb, capable of sending up shoots re-

Figure 44

Horse or Bull Nettle

peatedly from underground runners. The plant is covered with yellowish spines that make life miserable for workers in fields infested with it, especially when grain is shocked by hand. It is reported that heavily infested farms in the south are sometimes abandoned because the spines cut the legs of the mules so unmercifully. A closely related annual, the buffalo bur, is similarly armed and almost as mean to have around.

Some of the worst weeds in the cultivated areas of the United States include:

European bindweed or "Creeping Jenny"	*Convolulus arvensis*
Russian knapweed	*Centaurea repens*
Leafy spurge	*Euphorbia esula*
Nut grass	*Cyperus esculentus*
Bull nettle or horse nettle	*Solanum carolinense*
Perennial peppergrass	*Lepidium* (or *Cardaria*) *draba*
Canada thistle	*Cirsium arvense*
Perennial sow thistle	*Sonchus arvensis*
Quack grass	*Agropyron repens*

Any of the above-listed weeds, in absence of efficient control methods, are quite capable of putting farmers out of business.

Many control methods involve the use of chemicals, such as ammonium sulfamate; 2, 4-dichlorophenoxyacetic acid (2, 4-D); 2, 4, 5-trichlorophenoxyacetic acid (2, 4, 5-T); trichloroacetic acid, and many others. Several of these are selective in their action. Thus, lawn weeds can be killed in most lawns without injury to the grass by proper applications of 2, 4-D preparations.

Why are these plants considered bad weeds? In the first place, all of the plants in the above list are perennials, capable of sending up shoots from underground roots which contain large quantities of food reserves. They crowd out our cultivated crops, competing with them for food and water. Examination of an old stand of "creeping jenny" in a Midwestern state showed roots to the depth of thirty feet. That means there is no draught for a well-established stand of this pest. When all the crops have dried up for lack of water, "creeping jenny" is still green and flourishing and spreading mightily.

I once examined a field of corn partly infested with Russian knapweed. Where the knapweed was present the stalks of corn were shoulder high, and the ears as long as my hand. A yard or two away from the infested area, the stalks were eight to ten feet high with ears a foot long. Russian knapweed is a perennial relative of our common garden "bachelor button."

I know a nursery in northern Ohio that is badly infested with "creeping jenny." I have often wondered how many infestations have resulted from plants distributed from this one nursery.

Many of the weeds listed above are undesirable immigrants from the Old World. However, native American plants are not always well behaved when they travel abroad. Around 1839 someone sent an American prickly pear (cactus) in a flower pot to a friend in New South Wales. People there found the bristly alien effective for living fences. The prickly pear was all to cooperative. Like the camel who got his head in the tent, it kept edging in and spreading out until it had covered an area of sixty million acres. For a time it spread at the rate of one million acres a year. That is quite a weed patch -- an area roughly three hundred by three hundred miles. The people of New South Wales were literally on the way to being shoved into the sea by the spiny invader. The solution, when finally found, was simple. Insect enemies of prickly pear were imported, and in absence of hyperparasites (that is, insects that live on the desired insects), these spread even more rapidly

than had the cactus. In a very few years all that remained of the
pest were rotting stalks.

Many annual weeds also take a tremendous toll of our crops. A
city man once asked a friend of mine the name of "that yellow-
flowered crop the Iowa farmers are growing." My friend suggested
yellow sweet clover. "No," said the city man, "I know yellow sweet
clover. This crop has a little oats growing with it." This true story
gets a grim laugh among farmers over much of the grain belt of
the Midwest. The plant in question was mustard. In one year one
Iowa grain elevator removed a carload of mustard seed from farm
grain, and I doubt if that elevator cleaned one bushel of seed grain
in forty planted in the county. (One enterprising seed-cleaning-
plant operator heated his house for most of a winter with screen-
ings, mainly weed seeds, he removed from small grain.)

Another bad annual in the grain-growing areas of the Midwest
is buttonweed or velvet leaf, a relative of hollyhock. Seeds of this
annual are capable of remaining alive in undisturbed soil for as
long as fifty years. In other words, an infested farm has a long-term
fight on its hands. One Iowa farmer had ordered some soybean
seed from his local elevator. He came in to cancel the order. He

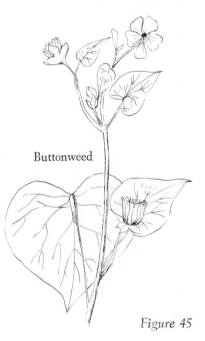

Buttonweed

Figure 45

had gotten soybean seed at a bargain. The elevator man examined the "bargain" seed and said, "This has lot of weed seed in it. Better let me send it to the State Seed Lab for examination; and don't plant it until I get a reply." The reply came back in less than a week. The sample was full of buttonweed seed. The elevator man phoned the farmer and said, "For goodness sakes, don't plant that soybean seed. It's full of buttonweed." "What'll I do?" asked the farmer, "I've already planted it." The elevator man replied, "Well, next time you come to town, buy yourself a nice, bright, new hoe and knock them off as fast as they come up." Buttonweed does happen to be very sensitive to 2,4-D which helps a little.

Every year tons of mustard seed and other weed seeds are harvested with the grain, stored and replanted. Although mustard seed is capable of living for long periods of time in the soil, much of that found in most infested grain fields is planted with the seed. Cleaning the seed grain with a good field spray program with 2,4-D would largely eliminate mustard from grain fields.

Other weed seeds that are common contaminants of crop seeds include dodder, false flax, foxtail, smartweed, Canada thistle, bracted plantain, quack grass, and button weed or velvet leaf.

There are quite a few weeds that are injurious to livestock. One

Figure 46

Witchweed with Insert
Showing, Magnified,
Attachment of Weed
to Root of Host

of these, St. Johnswort, is described in the chapter, "Borgias of the Plant World." Another related species, *Hypericum perfoliatum*, commonly called Klamath weed, introduced from Europe, has ruined thousands of acres of grazing land in the West. Like the cactus in Australia, Klamath weed (which is also rampant in Australia) is being brought under control by means of a beetle that lives on this one species.

There is an introduced honeysuckle, *Lonicera japonica*, that makes a miserable tangle of many woods, fence-rows and road-sides along our Eastern seaboard, and so must be considered a weed.

Witchweed, an undesirable invader from Asia, is semiparasitic on roots of grasses and can ruin grain or corn crops where it becomes established. It produces an enormous number of seeds and spreads rapidly. Fortunately, it is very susceptible to control with 2,4-D. So far it has been found only in the southeastern states.

Figure 47   Japanese Honeysuckle Covering a Woodland
                             Photograph by Edward Q. Cole, Jr.

The Chinese tree of heaven, common in many of our cities, should be considered a weed among trees because of its habit of sprouting everywhere and its unpleasant odor.

Tillers of the soil the world over have a constant battle with weeds. The slogan of the North-Central Weed Control Conference, in fact, says simply, "Agriculture is a controversy with weeds." Each year this battle places an enormous burden on crop production and adds to the price we must pay for agricultural products. The loss due to weeds in the United States alone was estimated at five billion dollars for the year 1955. Weeds occasion losses to American farmers second only to losses by soil erosion.

The control of weeds is a vast and serious problem. Many weed specialists work with the United States Department of Agriculture, with state colleges, experiment stations, the U.S.D.A. Extension Services, and with commercial companies in devising the most economical methods for the control or eradication of bad weeds. If you have a problem with weeds, it is a good idea to appeal to one of these organizations for help in learning best control methods.

FOR FURTHER READING

Ahlgren, Gilbert H., Glenn C. Klingman, Dale E. Wolf, *Principles of Weed Control;* John Wiley and Sons, Inc., New York City, 1951.

Bates, C. H., *Weed Control;* Barnes and Noble, 1955.

Crafts, A. S., and W. S. Robbins, *Weed Control* (3rd edition); McGraw-Hill, 1962.

Isely, Duane, *Weed Identification & Control;* Iowa State University Press, 1960.

CHAPTER 15

A Glance at the Fungi*

HE word "fungi," to the beginner, means mushrooms and toadstools. If asked the difference between them, he will probably reply, "Mushrooms you can eat; toadstoools are poisonous." Actually, these are two different names for the same thing. Further, there is far more to the fungi than mushrooms and toadstools.

The study of fungi is called mycology and specialists in the field are called mycologists. It is such a vast subject that we can do no more in this book than to offer a brief introduction. They are a fascinating group, and you may wish to pursue the study of them beyond what is offered here.

Fungi are plants that lack the green color (chlorophyll) found in most of the so-called "higher plants," and therefore cannot manufacture sugars by photosynthesis. They obtain their food directly, or indirectly, from green plants. Thus they use nutrients manufactured by, or modified by other organisms. Fungi are usually made up of microscopic strands called hyphae. The hyphal mass of a fungus is called mycelium. Fungi have no seeds, but usually reproduce by means of simple bodies called spores which are as fine as dust. Some of these are illustrated later in the chapter.

The use of spores for reproduction is not confined to the fungi. Many green plants, including ferns, mosses, liverworts, scouring rushes, club mosses, and many of the algae also produce spores. A few of the yeasts and bacteria produce sporelike structures. Yeasts and bacteria are sometimes included in the fungi, but are not covered in this discussion.

The classification "fungi" is based on general structural and on reproductive processes. It is entirely possible that relationships between the several groups of fungi are rather remote. The great

_____
*Some of the illustrations used in this chapter have been adapted, with the publisher's permission, from *Genera of Fungi* by Clements and Shearer.

groups of fungi here considered include the Myxomycetes, the Basidiomycetes, the Ascomycetes, the Phycomycetes and the Fungi Imperfecti.

The Myxomycetes or Mycetozoa, commonly called slime molds, have long been a puzzle to scientists. The name Myxomycete means "slime mold," while the name Mycetozoa means "fungus animals." Some scientists consider them to be fungi, while others class them as animals. These organisms have, in the vegetative state, a gelatinous consistency, but of different colors, depending on species. They flow slowly over fallen wood and through rotting leaves and soil, engulfing the food on which they live, digesting it, then flowing away from their own waste products. At maturity the gelatinous mass changes into various spore-containing structures, some of them quite complex and often very beautiful, although it is necessary to examine them with a microscope to appreciate their beauty. One species is fairly common on lawns, where the sporulating structures appear to the unaided eye to be a mass of soot. Another, common on manured plots or around dead stumps, resembles blobs of tan plaster when it sporulates. The spore-bearing structures[1] of the beautiful *Arcyria* and *Stemonites* species are not too hard to find on rotting logs and branches in stream beds or moist woods. These are shown in Figure 48. The sporophores of

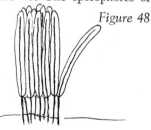

Figure 48

Arcyria   Stemonites

Spore-Bearing Structures of Two Slime Molds

the *Stemonites* species are dark in color and occur in closely palisaded[2] clumps, around a half inch or less in height. The

---

[1]These spore-bearing structures are called sporophores.

[2]To save the reader a trip to the dictionary, the word "palisade" is applied to an arrangement resembling many closely set posts, hence a palisade fence or the Palisades of the Hudson River.

Arcyria sporophores are lighter — a common color is a beautiful pinkish tan. They are borne singly, rather than in close palisades like *Stemonites*.

Certain organisms that have been classified with the Myxomycetes, possibly arbitrarily, cause important diseases of crops, for example, club root of cabbage and its relatives, and powdery scab of potato tubers. There are references on the Myxomycetes at the

Club Root of Cabbage.

Motile Zoospores, Greatly Magnified, in Insert

Figure 49

end of the chapter for readers who wish to sudy them further.

Most of the forms called mushrooms and toadstools are in the family Agaricaceae, in the larger group, the Basidiomycetes. However, the edible morel is in the Ascomycetes, and is discussed and illustrated with that group. The reader may want to know how to tell edible mushrooms from poisonous species. There is only one sure rule for separating them and that is, *learn to recognize the edible forms.* Discount all "easy" tests of toxicity. *Know what you are eating.* With this unqualified warning, we can make some

Figure 50

Common Field Mushroom (*Agaricus campestris*)

suggestions. The common field mushroom *Agaricus* (or *Psalliota*) *campestris,* is not too hard to recognize. The "gills" (the fin-like spore plates underneath the cap) are dusty pink in the young plants and rich purple-brown in those that are shedding spores. If there is a patch of these, you are apt to find both young and older plants and you can compare. All true puffballs are edible as long as they are creamy white throughout. There are inedible fungi that resemble puffballs, but they are gelatinous inside. The earthstar is a kind of puffball. The tough, leathery covering of this form splits open at maturity, the segments lying open on the ground in the shape of a star. You may someday encounter a giant puffball. These are edible as long as they are white throughout. They may attain a diameter of as much as two feet or even more. I found one with a sixteen-inch diameter.

Sometime, as you walk through the woods, you may encounter one of the coral fungi, which are species of *Clavaria*. Common also are the hedgehog fungi which includes *Hydnum caput-ursi,* the bear's head hydnum. If you are sure it is a coral or hedgehog fungus, it will be edible, although *Hydnum septentrionale,* which occurs only on hardwood trees, is too tough to eat.

However, as we said before, if you want to try anything at all unfamiliar, better examine the pictures and descriptions in a good mushroom guide rather carefully first; and it would not be a

Figure 51

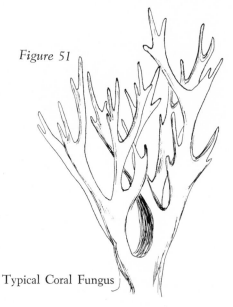

Typical Coral Fungus

bad idea to check with a mycologist. Occasionally, even the experts make a mistake when they gather fungi for food. The mycologist who checked this chapter tried the wrong mushroom on his honeymoon and, as he explained it, was "tolerably ill." My wife and I are fond of mushrooms, and I have had considerable training in mycology. I once gathered a large batch of *Lactarias,* none of which are poisonous. We ate them for dinner and they were delicious. However, I failed to note in the books that one species is a sudorific. That, in common language, means that it will make you perspire. The effects went far beyond that, however. In addition to perspiring, our eyes wouldn't focus, we salivated excessively, and our kidneys really worked overtime. I believe that each of us lost ten pounds of liquids, one way or another, that night. However, the next morning we both felt fine, which we probably should have, after a Turkish bath like that.

Examine the underside of a gill fungus (one of the common mushrooms). You will see the series of radiating, vertical plates or fins that we have mentioned before. Examination of these plates with a microscope reveals that they are covered with the palisaded clublike basidia. Each basidium is provided with four small tips on the crown, and each tip bears a single spore. The arrangement

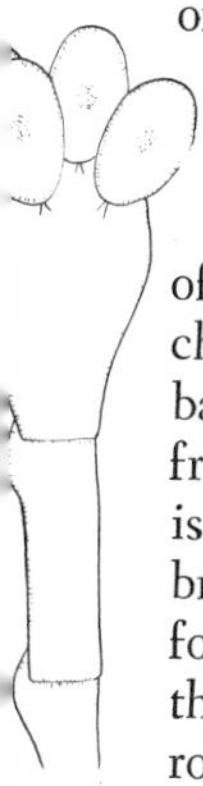

Figure 52

Spore Arrangement in Basidiomycetes (Basidiospores on a Basidium)

of four spores on each basidium, modified in some species, is characteristic of the basidios.[3] Once the spores are shed, new basidia continue to be formed. Spore discharge will go on steadily from the time the fungus is ripe until it deteriorates. The same is true for the pore fungi (Polyporaceae) which include the brackets on living or dead trees. The under surfaces of these forms are made up of a great many tubes, on the walls of which the basidia are formed. Fungi that look superficially like mushrooms but which have pores rather than gills (*Boletus* species) are also in this group. The gill and pore fungi release their spores in such a manner that the spores fall clear of the gills or pore walls. Because of this it is possible to make spore prints. Place the cap of a gill fungus, for example, with the gills a bit above a piece of paper for a few hours. The gill pattern will be traced with the millions of discharged spores. This is called a spore print. For white-spored forms, use dark-colored paper. Careful spraying of these spore patterns with a mist of liquid plastic will preserve them for future reference.

Sooner or later you will come across one of the stinkhorns. When you encounter one, you will recognize it from the name. It will look something like the horn of a cow and will smell like something dead. Several times I have come to the rescue of dismayed

Figure 53

Stinkhorn Fungus

acquaintances who claimed they had a dead rat — possibly under the porch — always undiscovered. I would simply locate and get rid of the stinkhorn fungus. One common name for one of them is "fetid wood-witch." Their evil odor is attractive to carrion flies and beetles that spread the spores. There are numerous related forms.

The rust and the smut fungi are in the basidios. They are quite different in structure and habit from the several species we have previously described. Usually we encounter the rusts as reddish or orange masses of spores on leaves of infected plants. Rusts are

[3]Mycologists, for the sake of brevity, often refer to the Basidiomycetes as basidios.

called obligate parasites, which means that they *must* obtain their food from living plants. There are many different species. Of these some exist on one kind of plant only, or on a number of closely related plants. Others pass through different stages in their life cycles on two distinctly different plants and are thus said to have alternate hosts. The word "host" is applied to the organisms on which a parasite lives. These alternate host plants are characteristically so unrelated that about the only thing they have in common is that they often grow near to each other. Thus, we have the following combinations:

RUSTS

Common Name	Hosts
Cedar-apple Rust	Juniper (red cedar) and apple
Stem Rust	Several grains and grasses and European barberry
Crown Rust	Several grains and grasses and buckthorn species
White Pine Blister Rust	Five-needled pines and several currant and gooseberry species

Many of these rusts are of great commercial importance. One of them, the very destructive stem rust of grain, is discussed and illustrated in Chapter 16. The cedar-apple rust infects red cedars (junipers) during the late summer, the infections forming characteristic lumps on the twigs. In early spring these form masses of orange or rust-colored jelly, on the surface of which spores are formed. These spores infect apples. There was a time when professional orchardists recommended red-cedar windbreaks for orchards. The results were pretty bad. In apple-growing areas red cedars are now ruthlessly destroyed. People in these areas who plant red cedars are frowned upon by nearby orchardists; if they do not voluntarily remove them, they may, one morning, find the task done for them. The "white cedar" (arbor vitae) which is not a juniper, does not carry apple rust. However, if you have apple trees, either fruiting or ornamental, on your property, do not plant common red cedars, or vice versa.

The smuts (Ustilaginaceae), another group in the basidios, are as widespread as the rusts. While they are capable of living, at least for a time, saprophytically (that is, not on living hosts), yet each species of smut has its own plant host and, as a rule, is more restricted to a single host for each species than are the rusts.

One of the smuts, occurring on corn as large, black masses, is rather common. To an Iowa corn farmer, corn smut is undesirable. However, these large smut galls can be cooked and eaten, again, as in the puffballs, before the galls form their black spore masses. They are a very popular food item in parts of Mexico, for example, and the Mexican Department of Agriculture has issued a brochure describing the best methods for infecting corn plants with smut.

The life cycles of the smuts, while not as involved as those of many of the rusts, are quite variable. The spores of corn smut, for example (they make up much of the black masses on the plants), are carried over winter in soil, trash or manure. These spores germinate in early summer to form still smaller spores called sporidia. The sporidia are blown by the wind into the funnel of leaves at the top of the young corn plant and infect the tender growing point. The infection develops slowly at first in the plant tissues and finally becomes evident as the characteristic growths on different parts of the plant.

Corn smut is in the genus *Ustilago*. Many of our grains are attacked by other *Ustilago* species, and by species in the genus *Tilletia*. These smut fungi form black masses of spores which replace the kernels and result in loss of crop and dirty grain. The *Tilletias* attacking wheat have another unpleasant characteristic. They release chemicals having the odor of dead fish, and for this reason are called stinking smuts. Contaminated grain must be carefully processed to remove the odor. Even then it may be necessary to dilute contaminated grain with large amounts of clean grain before it can be used. For this reason, grain containing stinking smut brings a much lower price at the mill or elevator, and sometimes it is not accepted at all. When wheat full of stinking smut is being threshed, the spores form a cloud around the threshing machine. Such a cloud of spores is inflammable and a chance spark may ignite it, causing a violent explosion, resulting in injury to equipment and operating personnel.

Smuts are spread by means of spores on the surface of the seeds in some species, for example, the stinking smuts and the so-called covered smuts such as oat smut among the *Ustilagos*. The loose smuts, for example the loose smut of barley, pass through the winter as infections within the seeds.

The first hint that anything could be done about smut on grain, according to history, occurred when a Spanish ship carrying grain was shipwrecked near the English coast. The farmers nearby rescued as much of the brine-drenched grain as they could, washed it, and dried it. Some they ate and some they planted. The germination wasn't very good, but the grain was relatively free of smut. Thus soaking seed grain in brine came into practice. This helped somewhat, but it was far from a satisfactory solution to the problem. Soaking in copper sulfate solution was found to be much better. Later dry applications of copper carbonate were used. A wet method employing formaldehyde was also employed. None of these methods appeared to be the final answer. Several years ago German scientists introduced a number of organic mercury compounds, for example, ethyl mercury phosphate, as seed treatments; and these are still widely used. Since the introduction of the organic mercuries, there have been developed a constantly increasing number of chemicals for the control not only of smuts, but also of other fungus and bacterial diseases carried on the surface of the seeds. Most of these chemicals, in addition to killing the smut spores, form a sterile "halo" in the soil surrounding the seed, thus protecting it from destructive soil fungi during the critical germination period.

Chemical treatment of farm seed has for a number of years been offered as a custom service by grain elevators and some seed stores. Special automatic treaters of large capacity have been developed for this purpose. A farmer can bring a truckload of seed grain to the elevator, dump it, drive around to the spout where the treated grain is released and in less than a half hour drive home with the grain not only treated, but also free of weed seeds.

The loose smuts that attack barley and other small grains present quite a different problem. The spores are shed before the grain is harvested and are carried by the wind to healthy heads of grain. There they germinate and infect the kernels. By harvest time the infection has penetrated the seeds so deeply that applying chemicals to the surface of the seed will not control the infection. Research workers found, however, that, if wet, the grain would withstand a higher temperature than the fungus. The method of control in use when I worked with this problem was to soak burlap bags, each about a quarter full of grain, in water; then agitate them for ten to fifteen minutes in a tank of water held at a temperature high enough to kill the fungus, but low enough to be tolerated by the grain, as I remember, about 130° Fahrenheit. I organized several barley-treating parties among Iowa farmers during my work there. Each farmer (usually from fifteen to thirty in a party) would bring a small quantity of his seed barley. We would work with two large watering tanks, one with cold water for presoaking and subsequent chilling and one propped up high enough to permit firing below the tank. The farmers would swish the partly filled bags of grain in the hot water to insure an even heat for the prescribed length of time. My job was to keep the temperature on the mark by alternate addition of cold water or more fuel, and to keep track of the time intervals. At the end of a day, all of us would smell like smoked herrings. More scientifically designed equipment is now used for the purpose.

The treated grain must be dried, at least partially, before it can be sown. Finding a place to dry it properly is often a problem. The work of treating the barley must often be performed early in the spring with night temperatures below the freezing point. The grain would be injured or killed if frozen while wet. Farm wives were often dismayed by having their husbands insist on spreading wet barley on the parlor floor to dry. One farmer of German birth, explaining to me his wife's objections, admitted that "in ein corner so steht ein piano" which, translated, would say that a piano stood in one corner. Because of the trouble involved, growers would treat a limited amount of grain (usually not over five bushels, and often only one or two). This grain the farmer would plant separately to grow smut-free seed. Even then he would have to patrol the planting during heading time to pull out the few infected plants that had gotten by the treatment.

Now let's leave the very interesting basidios and talk for a while about the Ascomycetes, commonly called the ascos or the sac

Figure 54

Morel

fungi. This is a very large and very important group. One of them, the morel, is commonly gathered in quantities for food in the spring. Its crinkly, pointed top makes it rather easy to recognize. The surface of the top is a carpet of the microscopic eight-spored sacs called asci. The same is true of the saddle mushroom and the

Figure 55

Typical Saddle Fungus

several species of cup or disc fungi that are rather commonly encountered in moist woods. Sometimes by gently breathing across undisturbed cup fungi, the flow of air (and probably also the change in temperature) causes myriads of asci to discharge simultaneously, resulting in a visible cloud of spores. Try this the next time you find a cluster of cup fungi.

Many of our plant diseases are caused by sac fungi. Still other species live on dead material such as leaves, cloth, or the like. One very common and destructive ascomycetous plant disease is the brown rot of plums, cherries, peaches, and other stone fruits. The powdery growth covering the diseased fruits consists of masses of asexually produced spores called conidia. These are capable of infecting other stone fruits. Infected fruits fall to the ground and become (except for the pit) masses of hard fungus mycelia. These are commonly called mummies. In the spring the mummies form small, stalklike growths wih cuplike enlargements at the top. These enlargements are lined with a carpet of asci or spore sacs that forcibly discharge the spores that will infect the new crop of fruit. A related fungus attacks lettuce and can become very destructive.

The unsightly black scabs on poor-grade apples and pears are are caused by still other species of sac fungi. Apple and pear scab fungi over-winter in infected leaves. Given a few spring days of warm, moist weather, the asci will forcibly discharge the ascospores. These spores infect the leaves of the host plant and

Figure 56

Spore-Producing Structures of Brown Rot Fungus on a Plum Mummy. At Right, Greatly Magnified, Ascus with Ascospores

result in the formation of the asexual summer spores (conidia) that spread infection through the growing season. The difference between scabby apples and U.S. No. 1 apples is a costly spray program to control scab and several other apple diseases and insects. That is why we pay a high price for a bushel of fancy apples.

A large and very important group of organisms in the sac fungi is the powdery mildews. These are so general that you have doubtless seen several of them, although you may not have been aware of it. They are obligate parasites, meaning, as we said before, that they are able to live only on living plants. They cover such plants as roses, lilacs, perennial phlox, dandelions, wild asters, and many others with a white, powdery growth which is made up of the external mycelium and the asexual spores or conidia. Close examination of infected leaves may reveal small, dark bodies in the powdery mass. These are called perithecia, special structures holding the asci. The appendages of these perithecia, which are microscopic in size, along with a number of asci in each perithecium, characterize the several different genera in the group.

The truffle, that delight of the epicure, is another Ascomycete. It grows beneath the surface of the ground as a compact mass. The French train hogs or dogs to sniff them out, and truffle hunters go through the woods with their animals on leashes.

This is an extremely brief introduction to the Ascomycetes or sac fungi, but for lack of space we must refer the reader to more specialized texts and turn to the next group. These are the

Figure 57

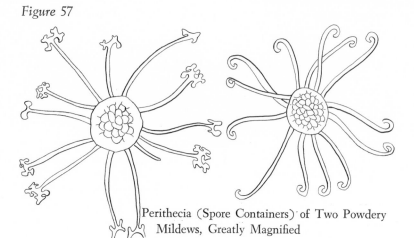

Perithecia (Spore Containers) of Two Powdery
Mildews, Greatly Magnified

Phycomycetes, more commonly referred to as the phycos, or alga-like fungi. These are rather less apt to be encountered by the beginning student than members of the two preceding groups, because so many of them are aquatic, and most terrestrial forms are not very conspicuous. However, there are a few species that are rather common, and several are of great economic importance because they attack our crop plants.

If you grow seedlings for transplanting, you may have an unpleasant experience with damping-off fungi, usually species of *Pythium*. Infected seedlings become softened at the soil level or a bit below and fall over. You can control "damping off" completely by baking the soil thoroughly and avoiding subsequent infestation of the soil. Infection of seedlings is favored by excess water and low temperatures.

The genus *Albugo*, sometimes called *Cystopus*, is rather easy to find, growing as a parasite on a number of plants. The common name for the disease and for the fungus is white rust, although the organism is not remotely related to the true rust fungi. The white rusts are obligate parasites, however, like the rusts and the powdery mildews. They cannot be grown in absence of a living host, or at least no one has managed it yet. Look for the following rusts as chalky masses on the underside of leaves, and if you can't find at least one by the end of a summer season, you have not looked very hard.

Species	Host Plant
Albugo candida	Radish, horse radish, shepherd's purse, mustards
Albugo tragopogonis	Goats-beard, salsify
Albugo ipomoeae-panduranae	Sweet potato, morning glory (wild or cultivated)
Albugo bliti	The several pigweeds
Albugo portulacaea	Puslane ("pusley")

The conidia or asexual spores of these fungi form crowded columns beneath the epidermis of the host. These columns finally break the epidermis and escape. Within the plant a more complex sexual process occurs, resulting in a heavy-walled oospore (egg-spore), capable of living through the winter and starting infection the following season. *Pythium* and *Albugo* are genera in the Peronosporales, in which group we find many other important plant pathogens. These include late blight on potato and tomato (discussed in Chapter 16) and downy mildews on grapes, lima beans, corn, sugar cane, teosinte, millet, lettuce, and watermelon. The downy mildew of grapes once almost put the French winemakers out of business and led to the discovery and use of Bordeaux mixture as a fungicide.

There is another large group of these phycos, the Mucorales. Of these the spun-glasslike fungus, *Rhizopus nigricans,* is quite common. Watch for it on rotting sweet potatoes and moldy bread. The small black specks you see on this fungus contain the asexual spores, or conidia. Do not confuse this fungus with such common blue, green, or black bread molds as *Penicillium* and *Aspergillus.*

Blakeslee, in 1904, working with *Rhizopus nigricans* and the closely related species *Mucor mucedo,* encountered an interesting fact. He found that if these fungi are grown from single spores, they never produce the resting spores known as zygospores that result, in these forms, from a sexual process. However, when he paired a series of these single spore cultures[4], approximately half of the combinations resulted in zygospores. In the formation of the zygospores the structures produced by each single spore culture

[4]The word "culture" as here applied, refers to a fungus (or bacterium) grown on a suitable nutrient material, usually called a medium (plural, media), in the laboratory. Media, obviously, must be suited to the organism being cultured. Beef broth, for example, is commonly used for bacteria. For bread molds, such as *Penicillia* and *Aspergilli,* and for many other fungi, a jelly made with agar (a jellylike substance prepared from a seaweed), water in which potatoes have been boiled, and dextrose sugar, is very satisfactory.

are, apparently, identical. It is impossible to tell which is male and which is female. However, if one culture is called plus (+) and the culture with which it forms zygospores minus (−), it will be found that all plus cultures will produce zygospores with all minus cultures, but that plus cultures will not produce zygospores with plus cultures nor minuses with minuses. The scientific term for such a fusion process, presumably sexual, in which two single spore isolates must be crossed to produce such spores is "heterothallism."[5] Certain closely related fungi have been shown, however, to be homothallic — that is, a culture resulting from a single spore will be capable of producing zygospores.

Choanephora cucurbitarum, in this group, is a spun-glasslike fungus causing rot of young fruits of squash and pumpkins (*Cucurbita* spp). You will be apt to encounter this in a squash or pumpkin patch, as it is not uncommon. Another relative is *Pilobolus*. It grows on the dung of grass-eating animals. The spore mass (sporangium) of this fungus is borne on a bulblike structure called

Figure 58   Spore mass discharged here

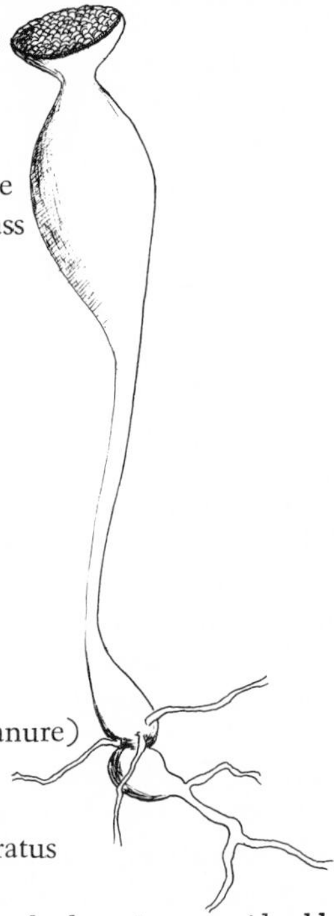

Vesicle in which hydrostotic pressure discharges spore mass

Mycelium (threadlike fungus strands in manure)

Spore Mass of Pilobolus and Discharge Apparatus

---

[5]In many heterothallic forms, on the other hand, there is a considerable difference between the male and female structures.

a vesicle. Certain particles in these inflated vesicles cause the whole structure to be pointed toward the light. When the sporangium is shot upward by water pressure in the vesicle, it is projected forcibly out of the depths of the debris in which it is formed. The surface of the sporangium is covered with a sticky substance that causes it to adhere to foliage on which it alights. Animals, eating this foliage, eat the sporangia as well. The spores are dropped with the manure, and thus the life cycle is completed. If the reader ever has occasion to work with plants grown on heavily manured plots, he will very probably encounter the sporangia of *Pilobolus* as unsightly, but otherwise harmless specks, mainly on the lower side of the plant foliage. Florists who have spread manure over the surface of flower beds frequently become dismayed when Pilobolus spots the foliage and blossoms of their crops.

Again, for lack of space, we must leave the interesting phycos and pass on to a very brief discussion of the last group we shall consider, the Fungi Imperfecti. This is a catch-all for many forms, not necessarily related, known only in the asexual or imperfect spore stage — hence the name. Included for convenience are several forms for which a sexual stage is known, but which are most commonly encountered in the asexual stage. The fungi included in this group are separated artificially into smaller groups on the basis of how the spores are borne, number of partitions in each spore, spore color, and other characteristics. Some of them bear their spores in enclosed structures called pycnidia, similar to the perithecia of the powdery mildews. The spores of others are found in a compact mass (acervulus) reminiscent of the cup fungi. Still others bear their spores in loose masses. Common bread or cheese mold (*Penicillium*) is an example. If and when sexual stages for these forms are found, they are usually Ascomycetes. Spores of the different Fungi Imperfecti are extremely varied from one species to another. If you have access to a microscope, examine some of these forms. They are often very beautiful.

Lichens should be mentioned in connection with the fungi. These are partnerships between certain fungi and certain algae. The fungus gives support and considerable protection to the algal partner, absorbs water, etc. The algal partner manufactures sugars and other foods. The enormous number of these is evidence that such partnerships are successful. You find them on tree trunks, rocks, and even on soil surfaces. The fungus and the alga are each a single species. For convenience, the partnership is given a species name too.

Some fungi are capable of causing infections on human beings and other animals. Athlete's foot is caused by one or more of several fungus species; ringworm of the scalp is another. In the tropics, many of these fungal infections can become rather horrible.

This account has only touched the surface of a vast and important field. Here are a few references for those who wish to study the fungi in greater detail:

FOR FURTHER STUDY[6]

GENERAL:

Alexopulos, C. J., *Introductory Mycology;* John Wiley and Sons, Inc., N. Y., 1952.

Bessey, B. A., *Morphology and Taxonomy of Fungi;* Blakiston, New York, 1950. (Contains a good list of references.)

Christensen, C. M., *The Molds and Man;* University of Minnesota Press, Minneapolis, 1951.

Clements, Frederic E. and Cornelius L. Shear, *The Genera of Fungi;* The H. W. Wilson Co., N. Y., 1931.

Gaumann, E. A., translated by C. W. Dodge, *Comparative Morphology of Fungi;* McGraw-Hill Book Co., N. Y. 1928. (Don't try this at first!)

Gray, W. P., *The Relation of Fungi to Human Affairs;* Henry Holt & Co., New York, 1959.

Rolfe, R. T. and F. W. Rolfe, *The Romance of the Fungous World;* Chapman and Hall, Ltd., London, 1925.

Snell, Walter H. and Ester A. Dick, *A Glossary of Mycology;* Harvard University Press, Cambridge, Mass., 1957.

MYXOMYCETES:

Hagelstein, Robert, *The Mycetozoa of North America;* Lancaster Press, Inc., Lancaster, Pa. (Published by author in 1944 and probably available through New York Botanical Garden.)

Lister, Arthur, *The Mycetozoa;* British Museum, London, 1911.

MacBride, Thomas H. and George W. Martin, *The Myxomycetes;* The Macmillan Co., N. Y., 1934.

BASIDIOMYCETES:

Christensen, Clyde M., *Common Edible Mushrooms;* University of Minnesota Press, Minneapolis, 1953.

Gussow, H. T. and W. S. Odell, *Mushrooms and Toadstools;* King's Printer, Ottawa, Canada, 1927. (Out of print.)

Ramsbottom, John, *Mushrooms and Toadstools;* The Macmillan Co., N. Y., 1953.

Smith, Alexander H., *Puffballs and Their Allies in Michigan;* University of Michigan Press, Ann Arbor, 1951.

---

[6]Many of the older publications are now out of print, but are available in larger libraries.

Smith, A. H., *The Mushroom Hunter's Field Guide;* University of Michigan Press, Ann Arbor, 1958.

ASCOMYCETES:

Ellis, J. B. and B. M. Everhart, *North American Pyrenomycetes;* Published by the authors, Newfield, N. Y. 1892. (Out of print.)

Seaver, F. J., *The North American Cup Fungi; Operculates,* 1928; *Inoperculates,* 1942; Published by the author.

PHYCOMYCETES:

Fitzpatrick, H. M., *The Lower Fungi;* McGraw-Hill Book Co., N. Y., 1930. (Out of print.)

Sparrow, F. K., Jr., *Aquatic Phycomycetes;* University of Michigan Press, Ann Arbor, 1943.

FUNGI IMPERFECTI:

Barnett, H. L., *Fungi Imperfecti;* Burgess Mimeograph, Burgess Publishing Co., Minneapolis, Minn., 1955.

Gilman, Joseph C., *Manual of Soil Fungi;* Iowa State University Press, Ames, Iowa, 1959.

ACTINOMYCETES: (*A special group not discussed in this chapter*)

Duddington, C. L., *Microorganisms as Allies;* Macmillan, 1961.

Waksman, Selman A., *The Actinomycetes, Their Nature, Occurrence, Activities and Importance,* The Ronald Press Co., New York 10, N. Y., 1950.

CHAPTER 16

When Plants Get Sick*

IR FRANCIS DRAKE is credited with bringing potatoes into Ireland about 1586. The crop thrived and soon became the principal article of diet for the common people. Around 1840 a strange blight struck almost simultaneously in different parts of Europe and North America. In 1844 someone from Canada wrote to a Dr. Bellingham in Dublin:

> Toward the close of the month of August I observed the leaves to be marked with black spots, as if ink had been sprinkled over them. They began to wither, emitting an offensive odor; and before a fortnight the field, which had been singularly luxuriant and almost rank, became arid and dried up, as if by a severe frost. I had potatoes dry[1] out during the month of September, when about two-thirds were either positively rotten or partly decayed and swarming with worms, or spotted with brownish colored patches resembling flesh that had been frost-bitten. These parts were soft to the touch, and upon the decayed potatoes I observed a whitish substance like mold.

The letter Dr. Bellingham received described "late blight," so called because it often attacks the crop late in the season when the weather is cool. The disease struck quickly and hard. In Ireland the horrible famines of 1845 and 1846 resulted. More than four million people in Ireland at that time depended on the potato for food. Of these, a quarter of a million died. Many who could find a way to do so left the stricken land and emigrated to other parts of the world. By 1909 the disease, caused by the fungus *Phytophthora infestans,* one of the Phycomycetes, had spread to every part of the world in which potatoes were grown.

---

*Many fungi cause diseases of plants. For this reason, there are a great many references to crop diseases in Chapter 15.

[1]This refers to the foliage of the plants, while the latter part of the sentence refers to the tubers.

186

Today, in spite of control measures and the use of blight-resistant varieties, the disease is still a serious problem in many potato-producing areas. The average annual loss in the United States for the period 1918 to 1938 was nearly fourteen million bushels. The same disease also attacks the related tomato plant. The inability of growers in Venezuela to control late blight of tomatoes in the rainy season once enabled me to sell a bushel of tomatoes, wholesale, for $12.50 on the Caracas market.

When the American pioneers first broke the raw prairie soil, flax was often planted as one of the first crops. As a rule the yield the first year would be plentiful, which would induce the homesteader to plant flax the second year, or even make payments on more land. Then would come disaster and heartbreak. The flax that yesteryear had flourished so beautifully soon sickened and died, and many homesteaders were ruined. Flax, it was said, was "hard on the soil." It "took too much out of the soil." However, it wasn't what the flax took out of the soil that brought about failure of succeeding crops. A fungus, planted with the seed itself, increased in the soil until flax could no longer be grown. Flax remained a crop for virgin soils until H. L. Bolley of the North Dakota Agricultural Experiment Station developed the first varieties resistant to *Fusarium lini*,[2] the flax-wilt fungus.

In eastern Iowa, near the Mississippi River, the sandy soil was found to be ideal for the growing of watermelons. Markets were developed and many of the people came to depend on the production of watermelons for the greater part of their livelihood. Then came melon wilt, caused by another *Fusarium* species. One small town, in its heyday, shipped out over two hundred boxcars of melons a season. Wilt cut this to fifteen cars. Many growers went bankrupt. Some moved away. Others stayed and learned to grow sweet potatoes. Eventually wilt-resistant melons were introduced, and production has been increasing for the last several years. However, markets, once lost, take years to become fully re-established.

Similarly, the farmers of California's Imperiod Valley had built up a great muskmelon industry, the greatest production center in the whole world. Powdery mildew[3] threatened to wipe out the whole crop. Mildew-resistant varieties introduced in 1932 and 1936 saved the industry.

The American chestnut tree, besides being valuable as an orna-

[2]This is one of the Fungi Imperfecti. Related forms, however, are in the Ascomycetes.
[3]Powdery mildews are described in Chapter 15 under the Ascomycetes.

mental and shade tree, was of commercial importance as a source of tan bark, timber, and edible chestnuts. Income from this one tree species amounted to several million dollars annually. Chestnut blight, introduced into America sometime prior to 1904, has killed off this noble tree until it now has little or no commercial importance.

The reader was given an introduction to the rust fungi in Chapter 15. The life cycles of some of these rusts are very complex. Take, for example, the organism causing stem rust of grain,

Figure 59

Stem Rust on Oats

that attacks wheat, oats, barley, rye, and other grasses, frequently causing partial or complete crop failure. A farmer walking through a rusted wheat field raises a cloud of red dust that soon turns his trousers rusty. These are spores of the fungus, and their color gives the disease its name. Spores are very minute structures, fine as dust, which bear much the same relation to the fungus as seeds do to our higher plants. This particular rust has several types of spores. The red spores are called uredospores. When one of them is blown to another wheat plant, it may germinate, if there is a sufficient amount of moisture, and infect the host. To do this the spore sends out small, threadlike strands called mycelia, that penetrate the leaf and grow through the tissues. So well adapted is the fungus to the host that host tissues are not at first killed. After a time, long, narrow, vertical wounds are formed on the plant, and from these exude masses of the red spores, capable of further spreading the disease. Later in the season a new type of spore is formed in the same wound, the black teliospores, heavy-walled overwintering structures with two compartments. In the spring a sprout emerges from each compartment. On each sprout are formed four small spores called sporidia. These are shot off with some force and may be picked up and carried by the wind. If they happen to come to rest on the leaves of the European barberry, they invade this new host. Only a few species of barberry, and the closely related genus, *Mahonia*, will act as host for this stage of the fungus cycle. Wheat, the "alternate" host, and even Japanese barberry, are not infected. On the upper surface of the barberry leaves are formed flask-shaped structures called pycnia, in which are formed myriads of small "pycniospores" that are imbedded in a sweetish syrup. Insects, attracted to this syrup carry the pycniospores from one pycnium to another and bring about fertilization (the process is somewhat similar to pollination and fertilization in our flowering plants). Soon after fertilization is complete, fruiting structures are formed on the lower surface of the leaves, and these bear the aeciospores, that are able to infect grain, but not barberry. Thus there are five spore forms in all: the uredospores that are formed on grain, capable of infecting only grain; the teliospores formed on grain, that allow overwintering of the fungus, and from which the small sporidia originate; the sporidia that infect the barberry; the pycniospores that function in the sexual process of the fungus; and finally, the aeciospores that carry infection from barberries to grain. The cycle is shown diagrammatically in Figure 60. The complexity of this particular fungus does not stop here, however. Certain strains of the fungus attack oats but not wheat, while other strains are confined to still other grass hosts. On a single host, such as wheat, there are many forms known as physiological races, one race attacking one variety of wheat but not another.

Figure 60

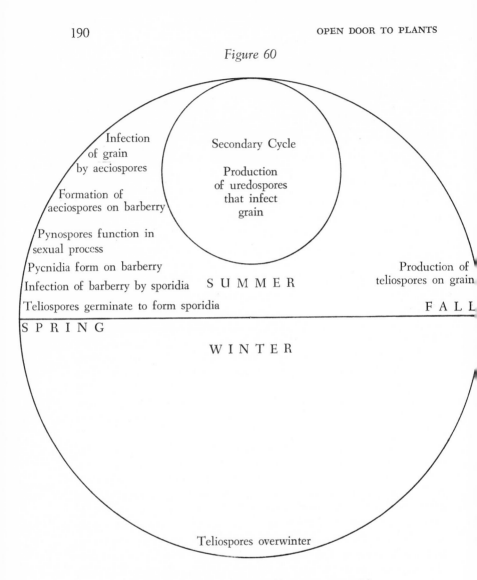

Life Cycle of Grain Rust (*Puccinia graminis*)

Because the rust fungus cannot complete its full cycle without the European barberry, the government has set up an enormous eradication program through the wheat-growing areas. One "barberry crew" in eastern Iowa came across an old farmer, away off the beaten path, who had a luxurious European barberry windbreak all along one side of one of his fields. The leader of the crew explained what the barberry plant did in the way of speading rust and how, by law, the hedge would have to be destroyed. The farmer said he hated to lose his windbreak, but if that was the law, to go ahead. While the crew did their work, the old man watched them and finally said, "Did you say that the barberry carried the rust to the grain?" "That's right." "Well, so that's why I was never able to raise any grain in that field. Year after year I would plant it, and year after year it rusted down. I never could understand it." The story is a typical one.

Even if all of the barberries are eliminated, however, there will still be some grain rust, because spores are carried north by the wind from southern fields where winter does not interfere with the continued production of summer spores. And so the grain breeder takes up the fight, endeavoring to produce grain varieties that are resistant to rust. Because sulfur dust controls rust, dusting of grainfields with airplanes has been tried and is of value when infection is heavy.

Fire blight was the first plant disease proven to be caused by a bacterium. T. V. Burrill of the University of Illinois guessed as much in 1878 and proved it by 1881. Some of the German scientists knew better, or so they thought. Bacteria, they said, could not thrive in acid media such as plant sap, so it just could not be. By the time they discovered their mistake, American scientists had made quite a few discoveries in this field. Moral: It is scientific to be skeptical but not to be dogmatic.

Fire-blight bacteria are spread from tree to tree by bees and other insects. Pears, apples, and closely related species are susceptible. Infected trees have large areas that look as though they had been blasted by fire, hence the name. Some varieties of apples and pears are much more susceptible to the disease than others. Once, in the Midwest, I met a man who had some choice apple trees on the back of his lot. He told me how the neighbors, burning rubbish in the alley, had injured his trees. The fact that the branches on the side of the tree away from the alley were also injured did not seem to have made him suspect another explanation. Because the neighbors refused to cease burning rubbish in the ally, the man had erected an enormous barricade of boards and gunny sacks to protect his trees — but naturally, it didn't help. In the San Joaquin Valley of California the growing of pears once constituted a major industry, but fire blight killed half a million trees within a few years, and the once thriving industry "vanished like a dream."

Viruses are the cause of many stunting, yellowing, and deforming maladies of plants. The cause of these diseases long constituted an unsolved problem in plant pathology. Beyerinck, a Dutchman, finally postulated a *contagium vivum fluidum,* an infectious living fluid, and thus started science in the right direction. There are still some people, however, who doubt that viruses are really living. In the first place, virus particles are so small that they can not be seen with an ordinary microscope, and it is rather difficult to examine them. They can, however, be photographed with the electron microscope. Some of them can stand temperatures up to 198° Fahrenheit, and finally, it is possible to crystallize some of them — a rather unorthodox attribute for living creatures. But on the other hand, they reproduce themselves in the host. Maybe we will just have to come to a better understanding of what is meant by "living."

An excellent example of the damage and loss that may result from a virus disease is well illustrated by peach yellows. There was at one time an enormous peach-growing industry in Delaware. The Reybold brothers alone at one time had 117,720 bearing peach trees near New Castle. Hundreds of thousands of baskets of peaches were shipped to Philadelphia, New York, and other cities each year. Toward the end of the eighteenth century trees in many orchards became unthrifty. By 1796 the situation had become so serious as to induce the American Philosophical Society to offer "for the best method, verified by experiment, of preventing the premature decay of peach trees, a premium of $60.00." However, peach trees continued to yellow and die. The disease, peach yellows, spread relentlessly. Slowly the great Delaware peach industry dwindled to almost nothing. More than a hundred years passed before the cause was to be discovered. Meanwhile the disease had spread to other peach-producing areas throughout the country. Peach yellows is still one of the worst diseases of peaches. Eradication of diseased trees and control of insects that spread the virus are of some help.

It is interesting that one virus is used. The multicolored, fringed tulips that are so decorative show these characteristics because they are infected with a virus known as "tulip break." However, tulips so infected are sick and each year decline in vigor.

Plants can suffer from diseases other than those caused by fungi, bacteria, or viruses. Take, for example, mineral deficiencies in the soil. Florida growers, several years ago, decided to drain part of the Everglades and turn it into crop land. The idea appeared to be sound, but once the land was drained, the farmers could not grow anything. Finally it was found that if copper salt was applied, the soil would raise fine crops. Mineral deficiencies in the soil are the source of considerable trouble. This is an enormous and very important subject and is treated at greater length in Chapter 18.

Crop diseases continue to levy an enormous annual tribute on the agriculture of the world. In the United States alone the amount is sometimes as much as three billion dollars a year. The study of the causes and control of plant diseases is the work of the plant pathologist. Today a great army of these specialists devote their lives to devising better spray chemicals, breeding resistant varieties, and, in general, finding the most economical methods for protecting our crops from disease.

FOR FURTHER READING*

Bawden, F. C., *Plant Viruses and Virus Diseases;* The Ronald Press Company, New York 10, New York, 1950.

Fawcett, H. S., *Adventures in the Plant Disease World;* University of California Press, Berkeley, California, 1941.

Garrett, S. D., *Root Diease Fungi;* Chronica Botanica Company, Waltham, Massachusetts, 1944.

Heald, F. D., *Introduction to Plant Pathology;* McGraw Hill Book Company, New York, 1943.

Hunger Signs in Crops, A Symposium; Published by American Society of Agronomy and The National Fertilizer Association, Washington, D. C., 1941.

Large, E. C., *The Advance of the Fungi;* Henry Holt and Company, New York, 1940.

Pirone, P. P., B. O. Dodge, and H. W. Rickett, *Diseases and Pests of Ornamental Plants,* 2nd revised edition; Ronald Press Company, New York, 1960.

Shurtleff, Malcolm, *How to Control Plant Diseases in Home and Garden;* Iowa State University Press, 1966.

Stills, W., *Trace Elements in Plants and Animals;* The Macmillan Company, New York, 1946.

Westcott, Cynthia, *Plant Disease Handbook;* D. Van Nostrand Company, New York, 1950.

*Many of the older publications are now out of print, but may be consulted in the larger libraries.

CHAPTER 17

The Never-Ending Fight
with Insects

ANY SUMMERS AGO I visited my grandfather's farm. He was nearly eighty. One day in the grain fields I found him sitting on some oat sheaves. He was holding a grasshopper between his fingers, swearing at it. To a boy this was "funny," and only years later did I understand.

Grandfather Craig, a Scotch immigrant, had taken up a quarter section of government land and a tree claim near what later became the town of Tracy, Minnesota, in 1875. With him were his wife and six children, ranging from infancy to about sixteen years of age. With the help of the older boys, he built a claim shanty. I remember that in my day it was used as a granary, and not a very spacious one at that. He broke the tough prarie sod, planted his first crops, and laid out groves and windbreaks on the wind-swept plains. Then came the grasshoppers in hungry hordes, ruining the crops and bringing heartbreak. Grandfather and the older boys went east to Pleasant Grove near Rochester, Minnesota, to work as teamsters, and thus earn money for a second attempt. They left Grandmother with the younger children and the babies to "hold down the claim" through the winter. The Indians were hostile through that section at the time. There were terrible massacres at nearby New Ulm, Lake Chetek, and Sleepy Eye. Prairie winters are seldom gentle. I recall snowdrifts as high as the cross-arms of the telephone poles during boyhood visits to Tracy, despite grooves and windbreaks on all of the surrounding farms.

The following spring Grandfather and the boys returned once more with enough seed and supplies to make a fresh start. Once more the grasshoppers came, bringing desolation. Once more the trek east for Grandfather and the boys, and the long, dangerous winter for Grandmother and the young children in the flimsy little claim shanty. Again spring came, and with it fresh hopes, fresh seed, and young crops. But once more the ravenous hordes of grass-hoppers swept all before them. Still another long, lonely, dangerous winter for Grandmother while Grandfather and the boys returned to civilization to earn enough to try once again. At last, on the fourth attempt, they got a crop.

The grim story of the pioneers and the grasshoppers has been told many times, but it is almost impossible to realize the heart-break and tragedy these insects brought with them. Many pioneer women were driven insane. Many of the homesteaders, unwilling or unable to continue the terrible struggle, gave up and went back East.

The Mormons, settling in Utah, were plagued not only by grasshoppers, but also by their relatives, the Mormon crickets. According to the autobiography of John Young:

> By the time the grass began to grow in 1848 the famine had waxed sore. For several months we had no bread. Beef, milk, pig weeds, segoes and thistles formed our diet.... As the sum-mer crept on and the scant harvest drew nigh, the fight with the crickets commenced. Oh! how we fought and prayed and prayed and fought the myriads of black loathsome insects that flowed down like a flood of filthy water from the mountains above.... I am sure that when the wheat was in head that it averaged two or three crickets on every head, bending them down. One couldn't step without crushing under foot as many as the foot could cover.

Many of the Mormons were convinced that the whole venture would collapse because of these creatures. The following account by Thomas Collister was addressed to the Historian's Office of the Later-day Saints Church:

> I give you an incident which occurred in this valley in the summer of 1848. When the crickets descended upon every-thing green, all the nursery trees had been destroyed, and much of the grain and the inevitable destruction of everything was apparent to all. President John Young, second Councillor to President John Smith, President of the stake, came to him and in the most emphatic manner said, 'Father Smith, it is your duty to send an express to Brother Brigham and tell him to not bring the people here, for if he does, they will all starve to death.' Father Smith looked thoughtful for a few moments and replied, 'Brother John Young, the Lord led us here and He has not led us here to starve.' So dark were the circum-stances that the hearts of the strongest Elders were faint. Elder John Neff, who was building a mill on Mill Creek, came to

Father Smith and said, 'Father Smith, I have stopped building my mill; there will be no grain to grind and Brother John Young advises me to stop wasting my money.' Father Smith replied, 'Brother Neff, go on with your mill and as far as I have property I will guarantee success; and had I sufficient means I would secure you against any loss. We are not going to be broken up and I entreat you to go ahead with your mill, and if you do so, you shall be blessed and it shall be an endless source of joy and profit to you.' In a very short time after this the gulls from the lake made their appearance and devoured the crickets.

It was these seagulls that almost certainly saved the whole Mormon venture in Utah. Another entry in the *Journal History*, June 9, 1848, explains this:

The first I knew of the gulls, I heard their sharp cry. Upon looking up I beheld what appeared to be a vast flock of pigeons coming from the Northwest. It was about three o'clock in the afternoon. There must have been thousands of them; their coming was like a great cloud; and when they passed between us and the sun, a shadow covered the field. I could see the gulls settling for more than a mile around us. They were very tame, coming within four or five rods of us.

At first we thought that they also were after the wheat and this fact added to our terror; but we soon discovered that they devoured only the crickets. Needless to say, we quit drawing the rope and gave our gentle visitors possession of the field. As I remember it, the gulls came every morning for about three weeks; when their mission was apparently ended, they ceased coming. The previous crops were saved.

The rope referred to was one of the few means the Mormons had been able to devise to save their grain. Two men would stretch a rope at a height designed to knock the crickets to the ground, then draw it across a swath of grain. The crickets, unable to fly, would take some time again to climb the stalks. The Mormons, grateful to the gulls, have created the beautiful Seagull Monument on their Temple Grounds in Salt Lake City.

People in New Jersey, Delaware, Maryland, and neighboring areas need no introduction to the Japanese beetle. This pest probably came into our country in the larval stage in soil balls attached to Japanese nursery stock. The larvae are similar to, but smaller than, the grubs of our common june beetle, to which it is related. The adults emerge in June and July. They are rather attractive insects, although when the householder or farmer has to fight them

Figure 61

Monument to the Gulls, Temple Grounds, Salt Lake City, Utah
(*Courtesy: Church of the Latter Day Saints*)

Figure 62

Japanese Beetles on a Peach (*Courtesy: Delaware Agriculture Experiment Station, Division of Ethnology*)

and suffer the damage they inflict, they do not become better looking with continued acquaintance. By the middle of August the bulk of them have disappeared, the females having laid their eggs in the soil. The larvae then proceed to do damage underground, feeding on the roots of plants as long as the temperature is sufficiently high, until they emerge the following summer.

Although the diet of Japanese beetles is wide, they do have their preferences. Mallows, such as rose of Sharon, hollyhock, and hibiscus, scarcely open their flowers before the Japanese beetles have eaten away the petals. Often there will be twenty to forty beetles on a single flower. Elm, sassafras, and certain other shade trees may be stripped of their foliage. A whole ball of beetles will keep corn silk eaten down to the husks or even further. For this reason many gardeners plant their sweet corn so that it will come into silk on or after August 10. Beans are another favorite food of these beetles, and peaches are often so covered with the pests that it is impossible to see the fruit.

Several methods of control have been worked out for this insect. Investigators found that the color yellow and the odor of eugenol (oil of cloves) combined with geraniol (which is part of oil of geranium) are very attractive to Japanese beetles. Specially designed yellow traps baited with these oils are hung by the thousands in areas of severe infestation, and beetles are caught by the hundreds of tons. However, many of the females lay their eggs before they enter the traps so this method of control has limited value, and still other control methods are necessary. Small parasitic wasps have been imported from the Orient. The adult, a skilled manipulator, stings the larva on the back near the main nerve center, attaches an egg, occasionally lunches a little on the grub and departs. In a short while the grub revives and goes on eating, but his doom is sealed. The parasite emerges from the egg, bites a hole in the grub and proceeds to feed on the body juices of its host. The beetle grub remains alive until the wasp larva is ready to enter the pupal state; then it dies.

Probably the most efficient control method is the use of bacteria that cause a disease of the larvae known as "type A milky disease." Nobody seems to know just where and how these bacteria become established on the Japanese beetle larvae, but probably they were originally parasitic on native grubs. In any event, these bacteria thrive on the Japanese beetle larvae. In utilizing the bacteria, hundreds of thousands of grubs are chilled, one at a time, in a cold stream of carbon dioxide gas to quiet them and then backed up to a special hypodermic needle device that injects into them approximately three one-thousandths of a cubic centimeter of a liquid containing the bacteria. The bacteria increase rapidly in the grubs. After a few days the parasitized grubs are mixed with talc, ground up, and made into a dust containing about forty-five billion bacteria per pound. The dust is then distributed over a few acres in each square mile of infested area. Further spreading is left to natural agencies such as birds, wind, and water. Commercial preparations containing these bacteria are now on the market. In a few years much of the soil in the beetle areas will have been inoculated with these bacteria. At the time of this writing the beetles have been much reduced where the bacteria have been distributed.

Farmers in the Midwest have a nasty insect to deal with — the chinch bug. These insects, unlike the Japanese beetle, do not have chewing mouth parts, but rather they puncture the tissues of the plant on which they feed and suck the juices. The adults are very small, a little less than a quarter of an inch long, but they are extremely prolific. The young (nymphs) are wingless, reddish

Figure 63

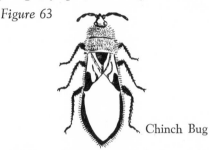

Chinch Bug

creatures that shed their exo-skeletons (outer coverings) five times before becoming winged, grey-black adults, feeding voraciously between times. Grasses are their food and barley is one of their favorites. I have seen whole fields of barley in which from a teaspoon to a tablespoon full of nymphs were swarming about the base of each plant. Finally the barley matures or dies without maturing, and the nymphs move *en masse* to the nearest corn field. Because they lack wings, they crawl, and the ground is alive with them. Their appetites keep pace with their growth, and by the time they arrive in the corn fields they are ravenous. A corn field can be utterly ruined by them in a very few days. Because barley affords an exceptionally favorable rearing-place for populations of these insects, farmers raising barley in some parts of Iowa were not at all popular with their corn-raising neighbors. In fact, the growing of barley has been abandoned in many parts of Iowa because of the chinch bug.

In areas of severe infestations it was once necessary to surround corn fields with barriers fashioned of strips of tarred paper placed with one edge in the earth and the other standing about two inches high. Along the barrier, at frequent intervals, post holes were dug. The nymphs, coming to the barriers, were unable to traverse the tar and, walking along the barrier to find a way across, would fall into the post holes. These barriers had to be maintained all during the migration period. Post holes became filled with insects with unbelievable rapidity. The trapped insects had to be destroyed and the holes reprepared. Dust rendered the tar barrier ineffective and more tar had to be applied. The advent of newer insecticides has simplified somewhat the fight against chinch bugs, as well as against the Mormon cricket, against which barriers were also used.

Some of our worst insect pests have changed their diet from certain wild plants or weeds to cultivated crops. The most outstanding example of this in our country is that of the Colorado potato beetle. Originally it lived on that miserable weed, the buffalo bur. Sometime in the past it moved onto the potato (both buffalo bur and potato are in genus *Solanum*), and it has been a costly pest ever since. The carrot weevil, which does damage to the roots of carrots, originally lived on the related wild sweet cicily.

The arrival of the Mediterranean fruit fly was perilously close to a tragic event for the United States. This nightmare among insect pests is pretty well distributed over the warmer regions of the world. The larvae or maggots of the insect feed inside any fruit (and many fleshy leaves and vegetables), utterly ruining whole crops. Our government entomologists had long been on the watch for it because it was obvious that our whole citrus industry would be very badly hurt if the pest ever became established.

On April 10, 1929, Dr. Wilmon Newell of the Florida State Plant Board was preparing to talk before the State Horticultural Society of Florida. The title of his paper was "Keeping the Fruit Fly Out of Florida." On that day he received a telegram from Washington saying that on April 6 Government inspectors at Orlando had found some suspicious-looking maggots in grapefruits. These were sent to Washington. The telegram confirmed the worst — the fruit fly *was in* Florida. Newell quietly went ahead with his talk, and meanwhile a small army of inspectors was rushed to the area to ascertain just how far the pest had spread. The dread news was released to the press on April 15. Immediately emergency funds were made available by State and Federal authorities. A tight quarantine was at once thrown around the region known to be infected and no citrus fruit was allowed to leave. By April 25 the whole state of Florida was under quarantine regulations with all shipments made under the strictest supervision. By May 2 Congress appropriated $4,250,000 to carry on the fight. An area of fifteen thousand square miles was designated as the eradication district; all known infestations were included in this region. The hub of the infestation was Orlando, which is right in the heart of the citrus growing industry. This area produces about seventy-three percent of the total citrus crop for the state. All fruit that had left the state was traced, and although some was found to be infested, the fly had not yet had time enough to become established elsewhere.

An immediate campaign was undertaken to deprive the insect of sustenance all over the area by the destruction of all fruits, cultivated and wild, and such vegetables as ripe tomatoes, eggplants, peppers and lima beans. The cooperation of almost everybody was remarkable. Everybody seemed to know what a catastrophe was confronting the state. The fruits were either buried (three feet underground, surrounded by lime and with a layer of oil on top of the soil) or put through machines to crush them, followed by steaming to kill the eggs.

The adult flies may live for as long as sixty days, which somewhat complicates control. Fortunately, two important discoveries were soon made: first, the adults are attracted to a bait containing sugar or molasses (more recently, enzymatic protein hydrolysates have been used) combined with some suitable poison, and second, this needs only to be sprayed over the tops of the trees where the flies habitually gather.

The battle was a grim one with State and Federal authorities cooperating closely throughout the campaign. The great fear was that the insect might become established in the Everglades or other uncultivated areas which would make their eradication almost impossible. Finally the job was finished, and quarantine restrictions that had been gradually eased, were entirely removed on November 15, 1930. The Florida citrus growers drew a long, deep breath. A small outbreak of Mediterranean fruit fly was reported in Florida in April, 1956. This infestation was eradicated at a cost of ten million dollars. (The new insecticides that had been developed subsequent to the 1928 outbreak helped a lot.) The State is now very thoroughly alerted to the fruit fly. Traps are everywhere, and carefully watched. An infestation in 1962 was quickly cleaned up.

In 1966, the Mediterranean fruit fly was once more on the march, this time in the lower Rio Grande Valley, near Brownsville, Texas, and Matamoros, Mexico, across the river. It is believed that the outbreak was cleaned up completely in forty-four days. Experience can bring about efficiency.

How wide-spread is the pest? All around the Mediterranean, several parts of Asia, Central and South America, Hawaii — it really travels far and fast. In this day of the airplane the fly can travel from one end of the earth to the other practically overnight.

Just how serious it is we have already indicated, but it is known to attack at least two hundred different crops, and it can ruin from twenty-five percent to all of the crop of anything it attacks.

Insects, like diseases, that attack our plants constantly exact tribute from our food supply. In the United States losses due to insects amount to about three-billion dollars a year. Insects often totally ruin whole crops. In man's struggle for existence it is entirely possible that insects are our worst enemies.

FOR FURTHER READING

Metcalf, H. O., and others, *Destructive and Useful Insects;* Mc Graw-Hill, 1962.

Westcott, Cynthia, *Gardener's Bug Book;* Doubleday, 1964 (3rd Edition)

CHAPTER 18

Plants and the Soil

HEN I was about sixteen I had a garden in our back yard. The soil was a black river-bottom silt that baked as tough as leather. There were about eighteen inches of this soil over river sand. It produced fair, but not good crops. We had a friend who was a blacksmith — that was back when there were still many horses to be shod. I had him save pure horse manure and hoof parings for me. Near our house was a strip of woods with plenty of leaf mold. I hauled home quantities of this. Then I dug an excavation about three feet deep, three feet wide and six feet long, and put together a mixture of the subsurface sand, the black, hard surface soil, the horse manure, and the leaf mold. When I finished, I could shove the hoe handle into that soil down to the blade. I planted two tomato plants in the prepared ground. Each of these produced more than a bushel of tomatoes. They should have — the two plants covered an area five feet wide by nine feet long.

My father told of a similar experience when he was about the same age. He got permission to garden a long-abandoned barnyard, where manure had been piled and allowed to decay for years. When he brought his first offerings to his mother — enormous beets and turnips — she told him, "Those are too old to be good. They'll be tough and woody at that size." But they weren't. They were tender and of excellent quality.

One fall I drove through certain of our southern states and saw miserable little cotton plants in field after field. It is true that there had been a long dry spell, but while I was driving past those fields, a picture persisted in my mind of a planting of cotton I once made in one of the rich mountain valleys of Venezuela. The land had been freshly broken from a tropical jungle. The soil was mellow, full of organic matter — with plenty of water available. The cotton plants were eight feet high, with easily twenty to forty times the yield of the poor blasted fields I was then passing.

These examples will serve to illustrate the importance of condition and fertility of the soil and an adequate water supply to the welfare of plants. Green plants manufacture their own foods — sugars, starches, proteins, and fats. However, to manufacture foods, plants need nitrogen and phosphorus compounds and several minerals, in addition to water, all of which must, as a rule, be obtained from the soil.

Many other factors are of importance in the soil in relation to plants, even over and above the presence or absence of fungi and animal life harmful to the roots — things like air, drainage, harmful products of decay as well as beneficial ones, and fungus and bacterial by-products. I can still hear the words of the great student of soils, Dr. Walter L. Kubiena. Technically, he was a micropedologist, a student of phenomena connected with the soil that are studied by means of the microscope. He said, "We have come to think of soils as merely a mixture of minerals. This is not true. Soil is alive." When we say that anything is alive, we have, with those same words, said that it is extremely complex, because all living things are complex beyond our complete understanding. The living processes that are at work in the soil are the result of many organisms functioning in a wide range of biological as well as physical and chemical surroundings.

In Iowa I once saw a field of corn on rich, well drained soil, and in good state tilth. The farmer had had it in clover the year before and had plowed this under. He planted the field with a corn hybrid adapted to and recommended for that part of Iowa. He planned to enter the field in the county ten-acre-yield contest. Farmers came from miles around to see that field. The grass was worn away beside the road by the cars of those who came, but not because it was a good field. On the contrary, the field produced less than ten bushels to the acre. Something had gone wrong beneath the surface of the soil — just what I am not sure — possibly an excess of nitrites, or the presence of a pathogenic fungus, or a large nematode population. Corn hybrids are fairly uniform. Conditions wrong for one plant would be wrong for all of them because of their uniformity. Neighboring farmers talked a lot about that field. The same hybrid half a mile away yielded eighty bushels to the acre.

In another part of Iowa one of my friends ran a farm with his father. They intended to plant one uniform field to corn. The land had been fall-plowed. One Saturday the father went out with the disk to stir up the surface soil. The son followed with the planter. When the father had about two-thirds of the field disked and the son about one-third of it planted, a rain drove them out of the field. The following Monday the father disked the last third and the son planted the last two thirds. They showed me the field at harvest time. Each third of the field represented a slightly different treatment: (1) disked, planted, rained upon, (2) disked, rained upon, planted, and (3) rained upon, disked, planted. The two outside thirds that had been planted immediately after disking yielded more than twice as much as the center third. Soil compaction, with resultant changes in oxygen level probably caused the reduction in yield. However, it is interesting to note that such a small difference in treatment could result in such great differences in yield.

When I first started to teach, I wanted to show my students what would happen if you burned soil. I brought some South Dakota earth to red heat and allowed it to cool. With unheated soil as a check, I planted the two samples with beans. How those beans grew in the "burned" soil! That wasn't what I had intended to show at all. At that time I was ignorant of the possibility of releasing locked soil reserves, such as phosphorus and potassium, and of ridding the soil of root-rot organisms.

Lakes fill in slowly to form bogs. The vegetation in these bogs does not decay very fast because the water does not allow free penetration of oxygen, necessary for decay. Therefore the half-decayed vegetation accumulates, often in beds several feet deep. When such bogs are drained and put into cultivation, the plants grown on them are actually growing in a huge sponge of humus material. Aeration is excellent in drained peat beds. Proper ditching will assure good drainage. Needed fertilizer can be applied and crops are commonly vigorous. However, in dry weather peat beds often catch fire and burn for days, and such fires are very hard to extinguish. One of the large peat beds of Minnesota burned completely. The owners, who had grown vegetables on it, considered it a total loss. One farmer, however, had an idea. Flax does not thrive where there are weeds. Pathogenic soil fungi (that attack the roots) are hard on it. The burned-over peat would have neither weeds nor pathogens, and the peat layer had not been deep enough for the fire to have left an excess of soluble substances in the ashes. This farmer rented the entire burned peat bed at a very low cost and planted it all to flax — hundreds of acres of it. The yields were enormous. A second year he planted the area to flax. Again he obtained enormous yields. He did not plant the third year. In two years he had made enough money to be able to retire.

As we have said, aeration and drainage are important for the development of plant roots. In Venezuela I saw sugar cane planted in furrows and the irrigation water allowed to run down these furrows. In fact, I have seen sugar cane planted where cattails would have thrived. I ran some tests with plantings on level ground on supposedly well-drained soil, and plantings on a ridge raised eight inches above the furrow. The yield was inceased ninety per-cent by ridge plantings. Venezuela has a six-month rainy season, and few cultivated plants thrive with roots in water for six months.

What elements must plants obtain from the soil? There are quite a series of them, and they must be there in sufficient amounts, but not in excess, if plants are to thrive. They must be in available form. If the roots of the plants can not absorb them, they might as well not be there. If one element is deficient with all the rest present in correct amount, the crop will still be a failure. Availability of such elements as iron, zinc, and magnesium is dependent on soil acidity. If the soil is too alkaline, these metals may be rendered unavailable in sufficient amounts. The following table shows correct amounts of the several elements for most plants.

PLANT NUTRIENT LEVEL FOR GOOD VEGETATIVE GROWTH OF CROPS AND PLANT TOLERANCE LIMIT[1]

| | Parts per million in soil extract | | | |
Substance	Field Soils	Greenhouse Soils	Plant Tolerance Limit[2]	Ideal Reserves
Nitrogen/as Nitrate (NO_3)	10-25	40	125	
Phosphorus (P)	1-2	5	50	15
Potassium (K)	5-10	20	50	50
Calcium (Ca)	100	100	200	
Magnesium (Mg)	5-10	10	50	
Sulfur as Sulfate (SO_4)	20	20	450	

[1]Taken with permission from "Soil Fertility Diagnosis and Control" by Charles H. Spurway, published by the author and available from Mrs. Charles H. Spurway, 436 Division Street, East Lansing, Michigan.

[2]The phrase "plant tolerance limit" means the maximum amount a plant can stand without injury.

Iron (Fe)	50	10-25
Manganese (Mn)	25	1-2
Aluminum (Al)	1	
Nitrogen as		
Nitrite (NO₂)	2	
Nitogen/as		
Ammonium (NH₄)	50	50

Some elements, such as boron (B), copper (Cu), molybdenum (Mo) and zinc (Zn) must be present in trace amounts. Often these may be fed through the leaves, and this may be advisable where soil alkalinity would render them insoluble and thus unavailable.[3] The presence or absence of a sufficient amount of these trace elements sometimes makes almost unbelievable differences in soil productivity. When the Everglades of Florida were first drained for crop production, no crops could be grown on the peat. It was found that the addition of fifteen pounds of copper sulfate per acre made the difference between very productive and unproductive land. Thousands of barren acres in Australia are being converted to productive land by application of as little as one half ounce of the element, molybdenum, per acre.

If any of the nutrients in the table are already available in abundance, applying still more in fertilizer is poor enonomy. It is well to know what elements are available in our soils in what quantity, and which are lacking. There are tests to determine this. Many states now test hundreds of thousands of soil samples annually for farmers at small cost per sample. Fertilizer companies also frequently offer such a soil-testing service.

The reaction of the soil — whether it is acid, alkaline, or neutral — is of great importance. Soil reaction is usually expressed as pH, a technical measurement based on acidity, as measured by hydrogen-ion concentration. A pH of 7 is neutral, above 7 is alkaline, and less than 7 is acid. Most of our plants grow at pH levels of 4.5 to 8.5, but many that thrive at pH 4.5 woud die or become unthrifty at pH 8.5, and vice versa. People who try to grow azaleas, mountain laurel, and rhododendrons on alkaline soil find that for best results

---

[3]The subject of minor elements in relation to crops is large and very important. The interested reader is referred to the symposium *Hunger Signs in Crops,* edited by G. Hambidge and published by The National Fertilizer Association in 1939. There are excellent color photos, showing different element deficiencies, in this book.

they must make the soil more acid. Soil reaction must be within the tolerated range for the crop that is being grown, and best growth will occur at optimum acidity or alkalinity.

If soils become too compact, not only do the roots have trouble penetrating the soil, but air is excluded. Ammonia, nitrogen in the form of nitrites, and sulfides — substances toxic to the roots — are formed. Waterlogging or water damage may even occur in sandy soils. I have seen whole fields of gladiolus on Florida sand with every root rotted off the corms following twenty-four hours under flood waters. Tobacco is another crop that is very sensitive to water-logging. It is hardly possible to stress too much the importance of good drainage and aeration for our crops. At the same time, it is important that the moisture level be optimum at all times.

Plants obtain carbon from the air in the form of carbon dioxide. Oxygen is available in elemental form in the air, and hydrogen can be taken from water. For most plants, all other elements must be taken from the soil. Each crop removes an amount of these. For example, a good crop of hay might remove from each acre:

160 lbs. of nitrogen
20 lbs. of phosphorus
120 lbs. of potassium
30 lbs. of magnesium
120 lbs. of calcium

Our crop plants must absorb these and other elements from depths no greater than their roots penetrate the soil, and as a rule this is not very deep. In the soil the amount of each required element, in available form, is limited. It is true that slow disintegration of rocks and larger particles will release, in available form, more phosphorus, calcium, potassium, iron, etc., but this proceses is very slow. Deep plowing will make available minerals in the lower layers of soil, but again we are faced with the immutable fact that the supply of essential elements in the soil is limited. These elements may be compared to money on deposit in a bank. Each amount withdrawn leaves just that much less. If a certain soil, for example, contained 3,600 pounds of available potassium per acre, it may be seen, by simple arithmetic, that thirty hay crops such as that described in the first part of this paragraph, would exhaust it. Obviously, too, the bigger the crop, the greater the amount of each of these essential elements that will be removed.

In a primitive society the produce of the land is consumed close to the place where it is grown. Excrement produced by man and his domesticated animals is returned, for the greater part, directly to the soil. As civilizations arise, urban centers spring up. Food carried to these heavily populated centers becomes excrement and waste products that are run into rivers, thence to the ocean. The valuable elements contained therein are lost to the land. Clean cultivation of the soil results in greatly accelerated erosion and leaching of soluble materials, and thus more of the land's fertility is lost to the ocean. Bacterial action in the soil is more rapid under the conditions of high aeriation in cultivated land than, for example, in the undisturbed soil of a forest. Thus humus, so necessary to good soil, is rapidly broken down. This is especially true of land cultivated under tropical conditions, where the temperature permits bacterial deterioration of humus twelve months of the year.

If soil reserves are exhausted more rapidly then they are replenished, there can be only one result — impoverishment of the soil. Because we obtain most of our food, directly or indirectly, from plants that depend on the soil, this means that impoverishment of the people depending on those soils must result. This has already happened in many parts of the world, all around the Mediterranean, in China, India, and over large areas in the United States.

What can be done about this? Nitrogen may be replaced in the soil by the use of such legumes as alfalfa, clover, soybeans, peas, vetch, etc. Certain bacteria form nodules on the roots of these plants and obtain carbohydrates from the plants, but in turn are capable of transforming the uncombined, unusable nitrogen of the air into nitrogen compounds which will finally become available to plants in a form they can use. Such leguminous crops will, as a rule, succeed only in soils with a sufficient supply of calcium and a pH near neutral (in other words, these plants do not thrive in acid soils). Lightning changes the free nitrogen of the air to oxides of nitrogen, and these are carried into the soil by the rain in form of dilute nitric acid, so that millions of tons of "fixed" nitrogen rain down on the earth each year. These two processes, if concurrent agricultural operations are properly handled, can keep nitrogen levels where they should be.

The use of manure will naturally occur to the reader, and obviously all manure and liquid excrement of farm animals should be returned to the land. But this is merely returning a part of what was taken from the land. Milk, meat, eggs, grains, vegetables and other produce still drain the land of elements that are not replaced.

Commercial fertilizers, of course, will replenish lost elements, but there is a limit to natural reserves of minerals containing such essentials as potash and phosphorus — and commercial fertilizers cost money. The study of these fertilizers, which to use, and how much, is a vast subject, about which thick books have been and are being written, and is beyond the scope of this chapter.

What crops could we grow if fertility and other conditions were ideal? Here is a list of theoretical maximums according to O. W. Willcox:[4]

MAXIMUM CROP YIELD PER ACRE WITH ALL CROP GROWTH FACTORS AT THE OPTIMUM

Crop	Maximum Yield Per Acre	Average Yields
Corn	(304.0 bu.)[5]	45 bu.
Wheat	171.2 bu.	20 bu.
Oats	395.0 bu.	35 bu.
Barley	308.0 bu.	29 bu.
Rye	198.0 bu.	13 bu.
Potatoes	1550.0 bu.	175 bu.
Rice	252.5 bu.	
Sugar Beets	54.0 tons	
Cotton	4.6 bales	
Sugar Cane	192.0 tons	

The average yield of these crops in the United States is usually not much more than ten percent of the theoretical maximum yields. If we grew tomatoes even as well as those I described at the beginning of this chapter, and used twenty percent of the field for roadways, we would grow forty tons of tomatoes to the acre. In New Jersey there is a "Ten Ton Club" whose members proudly boast of a yield of ten tons of tomatoes per acre.

Meanwhile we continue to spoil our rivers and lakes with sewage — sewage rich in nitrogen, potassium, phosphorus, and humus so fundamental to the growing of our food. Sewage can be processed and converted into commercial fertilizer. The Milwaukee Sewage Commission, for example, converts the city's sewage into a commercial product sold under the trade name Milorganite. By such practices we would not only conserve valuable fertilizer elements,

---

[4]From A.B.C. of Agrobiology by O. S. Willcox; W. W. Norton & Company, Inc., New York; by special permission.

[5]This yield was achieved recently by a teenage boy in Mississippi. It is above the theoretical maximum yield originally given in the table. The theoretical maximum yield must, then, be still greater than this amount.

but would also help to reconvert our rivers and lakes from sewage dumps to the beauty spots they have been in the past. The dangers inherent in the ruination of the soil are obvious. It is also clear that the greatest, in fact, the only important losses of essential elements from the soil are occasioned by running sewage and the like into the ocean and by leaching and erosion. Thoughtful people are coming to realize that if mankind is to continue to exist on this planet, these losses must be halted as far as possible, and that time is all too short for something very drastic to be done about it.

FOR FURTHER READING

Cook, Ray L., *Soil Management for Conservation and Production;* Wiley, 1962.

Teuscher, Henry, and R. Adler, *Soil and Its Fertility;* Reinhold, 1960.

Thompson, Louis M., *Soils and Soil Fertility;* Mc Graw-Hill, 1957.

Tisdale, Samuel L., and W. L. Nelson, *Soil Fertility and Fertilizers;* MacMillan, 1966.

CHAPTER 19

The Story of Hybrid Corn
An Introduction to Applied Genetics

YBRID corn seed production is a business grossing many millions of dollars each year. Most of the corn seed planted in the United States is of hybrid origin. Monetary returns through increased yields from hybrid corn have already amounted to more than all expenditures for agricultural research that has been carried on in this country down to the present day. This account tells what hybrid corn is, how it is produced, and why it is preferred over open pollinated corn.

By the time the white man discovered the New World, the Indians, by mass selection over hundreds of years, had developed flint, sweet, flour,[1] and pop corn. However, they had never progressed beyond mass selections. Robert Reid, starting farming in Illinois in 1846, was unable to plant his corn, a semi-gourd seed variety, until late in the season. This variety needed a relatively long growing season, and as a result his crop was very poorly matured. The immature seed, when planted the following year, produced a very spotty stand, and Reid filled in the missing hills with seed of a locally grown flint-type corn known as little yellow corn. After years of selective breeding from the resulting random hybridization, Robert Reid's son, J. L. Reid, developed Reid's Yellow Dent, the most important open pollinated variety grown on the prairies.

A. E. Blount of Tennessee, realizing that the ear parent contributed only half of the inheritance to the seed, covered the young ear shoots with muslin and then hand-pollinated them with "tassels" (the male flowers) of vigorous plants. By this method he developed

---

[1]The commonly grown field corn is derived in part from flour corn, with flint corn in its ancestry.

213

Figure 64

Corn Varieties. From Left to Right: Pop, Sweet, Flour, Flint, and Dent Corn. The Ear at the Right Has the Kernels Enclosed in Glumes, a Primitive Characteristic. It is Called Pod Corn. *(U.S.D.A. Photograph)*

Blount's White Prolific during the last part of the nineteenth century.

It was Charles Darwin who first wrote on corn inbreeding in 1877. Darwin corresponded frequently with Asa Gray, who wrote *Gray's Manual of Botany,* and told him of his findings in regard to inbreeding even before his results were published. One of Gray's students, E. M. East, became interested and began inbreeding maize in 1905 at the Illinois Agricultural Experiment Station. When he went to the Connecticut Agricultural Experiment Station in 1906, he took his experiments with corn with him and published his findings in 1909. G. H. Shull, working at Carnegie Institution, started experimenting with inbreeding maize in 1905. The increased yield he observed on crossing his inbreds led him to publish, in 1908 and 1909, definite recommendations for inbreeding and hybridizing as a valuable tool in maize improvement. Apparently both A. D. Shamel of Illinois and C. P. Hartley of the Bureau of Plant Industry did some work with inbreeding of maize shortly before 1900. Shamel reported in 1905 on yields obtained by crossing inbreds. Hartley also noted that crossing of certain inbreds resulted in increased yields, but he thought that other means of corn improvement were better.

Simply, inbreeding in corn is the pollination of the silks of the ear shoot (botanically, these are the pistils) with pollen produced by the same plant. This eliminates chance pollination by windborne pollen grains which may come from any corn plant. Corn may be inbred in either of two ways. The corn plant may be isolated from all other corn plants by distance or by other means

Figure 65

Corn Tassels Bagged in Preparation for Self-Pollination or Controlled Cross-Pollination (*Courtesy: Iowa Agricultural Experiment Station, Ames, Iowa*)

during the pollinating period so that there is no other source of pollen. A more practical method is to slip a small glazine or plastic bag over the ear shoot before the silk is formed. When the silk appears, the tassel is "bagged" with an ordinary paper sack fastened with a paper clip. Most pollen from other corn plants which may have fallen on the tassel will be dead in twenty-four hours. The next day the bag is agitated violently and removed, or the bag and tassel together may be removed and slipped over the ear shoot after removal of the glazine bag. The paper bag is fastened with a paper clip or stapler around the corn stalk to protect the ear. It is usually left in place until the self-pollinated ear is harvested.

What advantage is gained in doing this? To answer this question we must go into a little genetics, the science dealing with the manner in which various organisms inherit their characteristics from their parents. A detailed account of just what happens in plant cells[2] prior to and during the reproductive process is rather involved, and will be omitted from our discussion. If you want to get into it deeper, there are several excellent texts on the subject.[3] Simply stated, in each cell there are bodies called nuclei (singular, nucleus) that control cell multiplication, commonly called cell division and, in certain cells, reproduction. In these nuclei occur a definite number of bodies called chromosomes, and these chromosomes contain, in definite locations on each chromosome, still smaller bodies called genes. These genes have the power to determine the characteristics of the organism. In corn, for example, they would determine whether the plant would normally be tall or short, the kernels yellow or white, the cobs white or red, etc.

The nucleus of each cell not immediately involved in reproduction has a *double set* of chromosomes and, therefore, a double set of genes. When a plant is ready to reproduce, special cells are formed in which the nuclei contain a single set of chromosomes. In the process of forming such nuclei the paired genes of the original double set of chromosomes are distributed somewhat at random in each single chromosome series. In seed plants the reproductive

---

[2] Almost all plants and animals are made up of microscopic "cells," which are the fundamental work units of the organism. Many similar cells make up tissues. Tissues that work together make up organs. Organs that work together make up systems (for example, the digestive system), and the whole organism is the sum of its systems.

[3] For example, *Cytology and Cytogenetics*, by Carl P. Swanson; Prentice-Hall, Inc., Englewood Cliffs, N. J., 1957.

cells, which are found in pollen grains and in the "egg" cell of what will become the seeds (the egg cells are called "ovules"), each contain this half-number of chromosomes, and of course the half-number of genes. Following pollination, the nucleus of the pollen grain fuses with the reproductive nucleus of the ovule, and once again we have the double chromosome — double gene set arrangement. It should be clear that each parent will thus have contributed half of the genes, and will therefore have contributed half of the determinants for the characteristics of the offspring. All sexual reproduction in plants and animals works this way.

Now let us see how this works in the inbreeding of corn. Let us trace some of the genes that determine plant characteristics by labeling them A, B, C, D, etc. Keep in mind that there are two sets of these in the nuclei of cells that are not immediately involved in reproduction. For our example, let us assume that, in each pair, the genes are different. Then we would have something like this:

A   B   C   D   E   F   G   H   I   J   K   L   M   N
A' B' C' D' E' F' G' H' I' J' K' L' M' N'

through all the genes — and there are quite a number of them. If these genes are distributed at random in the nucleus of the pollen grain and the nucleus of the egg cell of the ovule, we might have a distribution somewhat like this:

Pollen grain A   B   C' D   E' F   G' H' I   J' K   L' M   N'
Ovule   A' B   C' D' E' F   G   H' I' J   K' L   M   N'

If we self-pollinated this corn plant, as described earlier in this chapter, you can see that on the average about half of the gene pairs would come out alike. If this were repeated, about half of the remaining gene pairs would then be alike, or seventy-five percent of the total. If we continued to inbreed, we would get nearer and nearer to one hundred percent *like* gene pairs. The closer we come to one hundred percent like pairing of genes, the more uniform the "inbred line" of maize becomes. In fact, it tends to become a fixed entity, with about as little variation between plants as a row of pins from the same machine, and it will tend to remain so as long as we continue inbreeding.

It is known that genes are subject to occasional, and often drastic, changes. Such a change, called a mutation, may produce a mutant — an offspring very different from either parent. Mutations, if they appear undesirable, can be removed from the population prior to reproduction.

The inbred thus produced is characteristically weaker and less productive than the open-pollinated ancestors. Apparently the interaction of certain of the paired genes in the two sets tends, as a general rule, to make for greater vigor than does a full set of identical genes. In fact, some of the lines being inbred become so feeble that it is impossible to maintain them, and they die out. However, there are a few very vigorous inbred lines.

Once corn breeders have created a large number of inbred lines, they make a great number of crosses and then watch for results in the offspring or progeny. The hybridizer says that some of the crosses "nick," while others fail to "nick." By this they mean that the cross is favorable or unfavorable. Naturally, only favorable crosses are used in further work. The result of the crossing of two inbreds is called a single cross. Commercially these are made by planting, in a well-isolated field, two rows of female parents for each row of male parents. The tassels of the female rows are removed, so that all of the pollinating is done by the male rows.

It is somewhat expensive to produce single-cross seed; the low vigor of the inbreds results in a poor yield of seed. In fact, it isn't very feasible commercially. This problem was solved by Donald Jones, a student of Edward East at the Connecticut Agricultural Experiment Station. You will recall that Mr. East was mentioned earlier in the chapter. Jones took over the corn-breeding experiments from Mr. East in 1915. His solution to this problem of commercial seed production was simplicity itself — he crossed single crosses. These, being much more vigorous than inbreds, produced high yields of seed. Further, they are vigorous enough so that one row of pollen parent will pollinate three rows of ear parents. All that was necessary was to find what single crosses would nick well. Jones further contributed a valuable bit of theory to the subject. Prior to his work, it was thought that what is called "hybrid vigor" resulted merely from the act of hybridizing. Jones contended that hybrid vigor is due to the contribution of favorable genes by each parent, and this seems to be the case.

Hybrid corn well adapted to the conditions under which it is grown frequently yields thirty percent more than open-pollinated varieties. Further, once a valuable double cross has been produced, we may then reproduce it whenever we wish by going back to those fixed entities, the inbreds. By suitable inbreeding and hybridizing it is possible not only to increase yields, but also to insure in the maize plant many other desirable characteristics, such as resistance to cold, to disease, to insect damage, and to lodging (breaking over of the plant at maturity). We may control the starchiness, flintiness, or oiliness of the kernels. We may control the length of time required for maturity. We may breed maize varieties suitable for certain special soils, or obtain many other desirable characteristics. Although the production of hybrid seed is rather simple with corn, the same principles are applicable, with suitable modifications, to many other crops.

FOR FURTHER READING

Pierre, Wm. H., et al., *Advances in Corn Production;* Iowa State University Press, 1966.

CHAPTER 20

Trees, Forests and Man

NYONE interested in nature is interested in trees. However, the full importance in our lives of trees and forests and of the products obtained from them may not be immediately apparent. From a monetary standpoint alone, their importance is enormous. Well over six percent of our national income is derived from products of the forest, products including not only lumber and paper pulp, but also tanning materials, raw materials for plastics, turpentine, insulating materials, and materials for thousands of other uses.

The most important single service forests render to mankind is that of literally holding the land together. Soil denuded of forest and other plant cover can be washed to ruin in a very short time. This has already happened over much of the world, and still continues at a terrifying rate. I have seen hundreds of square miles of rocky desert in Venezuela, for example, with here and there a remnant island, often no larger than a table top, of rich black soil two feet deep. There are many parts of the United States where the land has already been so badly eroded that hundreds or even thousands of years will be necessary to repair the damage. The conditions of poverty found all around the Mediterranean and over much of China and India have resulted in part from such erosion.

With eroded, bare slopes come destructive floods, which would never have occurred had the forests with their spongy humus covering been left in possession of the watersheds. In the winter of 1961-62 a denuded mountain slope in South America slid down, following heavy rains, and wiped out an entire village. The destructive floods that tear so frequently at the vitals of China are also directly traceable to deforestation.

The importance of forest coverage in storing water and maintaining adequate water supplies has long been realized, and many of our cities have very carefully provided for the protection of the watersheds upon which their water supplies depend. Extensive forests (and other vegetative cover) exert a beneficial effect on weather conditions. Many parts of the world now desert were once rich with tropical vegetation.

The importance of forests in relation to the beauty of our country and to recreational uses is not to be measured in money alone. Most of us plan each year for a vacation in some woodsy spot — the more beautiful and unspoiled, the better. However, sad to say, many who visit such places are not careful about leaving the beauty of the woods unspoiled.

To those for whom hunting and fishing are valued sources of recreation, the forests are of extreme importance. Most of our lakes and streams, which we include in our recreational areas, would be dismal and unproductive affairs if it were not for the forests that surround and protect them from the devastation of erosion.

Even from the monetary point of view, the use of our forests for recreational purposes is vastly important. With thirty-five million people visiting our national parks each year, with fifteen million hunting licenses and eighteen million fishing licenses issued annually, it is obvious that the recreational use of our forests and their lakes and streams involves the exchange of vast sums of money — possibly as much as five percent of the national income.

The continued welfare of our nation demands that we preserve, protect, extend, and use wisely our forest resources. We still consume annually at least half again as much lumber as we are growing. In spite of the increasingly extensive use of raw materials other than wood in our technology, the drain on our forests, far from decreasing, is continually increasing.

The lumber industry itself has become increasingly concerned with the elimination of waste in lumbering operations — especially if such economies can result in new sources of profit.[1] Shavings, sawdust, limbs, and dead trees are used for paper pulp. Lignin, one of the constitutents of wood, still presents a challenge, but alcohol and sugar can both be obtained from wood, and their production may eventually become industries of great importance. Tree bark, once almost totally wasted, is now made into insulation materials, felts, roofing, soil conditioners, etc. Where formerly thirty percent

---

[1]See, for example: "Timber Industry Sprouts New Shoots," *Business Week,* July 30, 1955, p. 103, and "Facts About the Nation's Lumber Industry," 1955 Edition, American Forest Products Industries, Inc., 1816 North Street, N.W., Washington, D.C.

of the felled tree was used, now seventy percent is used, and this tendency toward more complete utilization continues to increase.

To gain an idea of the vastness of the lumber industry in the United States, we should remember that the country used 12,211,-671,000 board feet of lumber in 1953, of which 2,770,505,000 were imported. This amounts to 240 board feet per person per year. Only New Zealand, with a per capita consumption of 280 board feet, exceeded the United States in this respect.

There are many other great industries, both here and abroad, that are based on products of the forests. Some of these are practically unknown to us. 300,000,000 pounds of cork are harvested annually, to be used in making floats, insulation, stoppers, linoleum, etc. The great rubber industry still utilizes large amounts of latex from rubber trees in spite of the increasing use of synthetic products. *Hevea braziliensis,* a relative of poinsettia and castor bean, is the most important source of natural rubber latex by far, although some is obtained from a fig relative, *Ficus elastica,* and the related Castillia elastica. The latter is commonly called *caucho* (rubber) in Venezuela. It was heavily exploited during the last war when our supply of *Hevea* rubber from the East Indies and Malaya was cut off.

The production of chicle, from which chewing gum is made, is no small industry. The tree from which it is obtained, *Achras sapota,* in the tropical family *Sapotaceae,* is native to South America. Other trees in this family supply similar substances. A great many trees over the world, especially certain legumes, supply gums such as gum arabic, gum tragacanth (used in cosmetics) and others. Resins (used in varnishes), lac (used in shellac), tanning substances, and many, many other commercially important products come from trees.

Returning to the problem of forest conservation, it is possible for our country to maintain itself in a healthy condition of self-sufficiency in the matter of forests and the products and services obtained from them. Because of the economic and recreational importance of our forests, the government has wisely established many tracts as national forest reserves. A United States Forest Service, devoted to maintaining them in a maximum state of beauty and productivity, has been created. Working cooperatively with the Forest Service are many individuals and organizations[2] that realize the

---

[2] It is significant that our national and international service organizations are taking an active role in relation to conservation practices. Kiwanis In-

importance of our forests to our very life as a great nation. Many of the more progressive lumber and paper companies and others interested in the products of the forests are now in the vanguard of the movement for wiser long-term use of forest resources. These public-spirited individuals and organizations are leading a constant and unrelenting battle with the avaricious interests that would cash the nation's resources for a quick profit.

The history of efforts toward forest conservation dates back well before 1700. Although the Germans were the first to establish forestry on a scientific basis, many great men in the United States have been interested in soil and forest conservation. As long ago as 1681 William Penn signed an ordinance requiring that, on clearing land, one acre in five was to be left in forest. Both Washington and Jefferson were good conservationists. Each of them practiced contour plowing to protect the land against erosion. John Quincy Adams established a forest reserve in 1828 near Pensacola, Florida[3]. This land was later removed from conservation by Andrew Jackson, which shows that not all of our leaders have been far-sighted.

In 1875 a citizens' group met in Chicago to organize the American Forestry Association, one purpose of which was to further the cause of forest conservation. Soon after this the Department of Agriculture was authorized by Congress to appoint a forest agent. Dr. Franklin B. Hough of Lowell, Massachusetts, had long been active in movements to protect our forests; and he was wisely selected to be the first to fill this position. Carl Schurz, a German immigrant, was appointed Secretary of the Interior in 1877, and under his direction the whole idea of great national reserves expanded rapidly.

Theodore Roosevelt and his able associate, Gifford Pinchot, who served as Roosevelt's Chief Forester, made by far the greatest early contributions to forest, grassland, and national park conservation. These two, with the help of many far-sighted citizens, and against the opposition of many greedy and short-sighted ones, eventually were responsible for the creating of 234,000,000 acres in national reserves. Roosevelt opened one of his speeches before a group of conservationists with the direct and simple statement, "I am against the man who skins the land." Conservation is an important subject on which much has been written. For the reader

---

ternational, for example, has a well-organized program for the furtherance of conservation.

[3]His primary concern was an assured supply of oak lumber for our navy.

interested in pursuing it further, there are valuable references at the end of the chapter.

As for the trees that surround us and make up our forests, the plant lover will wish to become familiar with these as soon as possible if he has not already done so. An introduction to tree identification may be found in Chapter 2.

The love of beautiful wood has a long history. The Bible repeatedly recites the kinds of woods used in construction of buildings, altars, and the ark of the covenant, in connection with worship. Nor is the love of fine woods confined to civilized peoples. Beautiful woods have been a favorite medium for fine craftwork among primitive peoples since time out of mind, and much of what they have produced is of excellent quality. The regard that the primitive peoples have for beautiful woods is illustrated by the fact that the use of pink ivory, a wood growing in South Africa, is still taboo in some districts to anyone other than the chiefs.

Black walnut, native to North America, is one of the world's most beautiful woods. It is so highly prized that a number of foreign woods resembling it are called walnut. Black cherry, native to North America, is also beautiful. Much of the cherry furniture of the past was stained a bright red, which is unfortunate because natural black cherry becomes a very lovely nut-brown on aging. Oregon myrtle, which is not true myrtle but rather a relative of sassafras, cinnamon, and camphor, is, in its natural state, a beautiful, lustrous blonde wood. If held submerged in water for some time, it takes on a very attractive darker color and is then called black myrtle.

The walnut that was once so abundant in the United States has, in the past, often been shamelessly wasted or misused. Much was burned as stove wood or split for fence rails. I have made furniture from black walnut which had originally been used to frame a barn in Illinois.

Unfortunately, the range of beauty in woods is not widely known. Many people are reasonably familiar with black walnut and mahogany, but most people will not recognize natural cherry. Quite a few people know that a black wood is probably ebony. The widespread use of bird's eye maple a few years back enabled many to become familiar with this wood. Circassian walnut burl plaques were used as veneer on many pieces of furniture around 1900-1910. A few of the elite know about pearwood, satinwood, and white mahogany (which is not a mahogany). For a number of years I have experimentally asked the question from time to time, "What color is teak?" The answer almost invariably is "black." Unless teak is stained, its natural color is sort of a greenish-yellowish brown. Much that is accepted as walnut in cheaper furniture is dyed gum-wood.

While a few choice woods are native to the United States, most of them grow in the tropics, and their number is enormous. Many tropical trees with beautiful wood are too small or too rare to enter into the commerce of the world. For example, desert ironwood, growing in the arid regions of the southwest, is beautiful enough to be used in jewelry, but is not a commercially exploited wood. The lumberman, like any other businessman, wants to make the most profit for capital and effort invested; and if he can not get enough board feet of lumber from a log to warrant the expense of handling it, he will leave it, no matter how beautiful. Further, sad to say, if the tree is large and has beautiful wood, but a wood that is unknown and therefore not in demand, he will be apt to leave that one too.

The bean family (Leguminosae) supplies about one-fourth of the world's fine woods. Here we find rosewood from South America and East Indian rosewood (*Dalbergia*). There are many other *Dalbergia* species with beautiful wood. Most of these have a dark, rich, purplish color and interesting markings. However, one of the *Dalbergias*, African blackwood, would be mistaken by the novice for ebony. Cocobola, used for the handles of fine kitchen knives, is obtained from several *Dalbergia* species in Central America.

Pernambuco, zebrawood, all of the acacias, and padauk are also legumes. Pernambuco gets its name from the South American port from which it is shipped. It is a rich orange color, strong, hard, and heavy. It has long been used for making violin bows. Zebrawood comes from Central Africa. Its appearance is startling, tan with brown stripes, and it is much used for very vigorous effects. Padauk, which is a rich red brown when aged, originally came from the Orient. The high cost of the Oriental species has led to its substitution by the similar and related red sanders of Africa which is now marketed as padauk. However, the Asiatic species (Andaman padauk) is the better of the two. The old Pullman cars were finished in padauk.

The mahogany family (the Meliaceae) supplies a large number of species of fine woods. There are a few of these that are as good as, or possibly even better than, true mahogany — for example, the Australian maple silkwoods (*Flindersia species*) with high figure.

If a wood is called mahogany with no qualification, such as

"African," "Honduras," or "Philippine," the word should be applied strictly to the true mahogany which is native to southern Florida, the Keys, and the West Indies. The true mahogany may be seen growing as a boulevard tree in Miami at the present time. However, lumber from this species is no longer common. Most of the wood sold as mahogany is from a related mainland species, or some of the related *Khaya* species of Africa. Philippine mahogany is not a mahogany, but belongs to an unrelated Asiatic family, the Dipterocarpaceae, and is definitely inferior.

True mahogany is harder, heavier, and closer grained than the South American mainland mahoganies, which are commonly sold as Honduras or Mexican mahogany. Unstained, it is a rich dark brown color. The South American and African mahoganies usually become red brown, rather than brown, after exposure of the finished wood to light for some time.

The history of the cutting of mahogany is about what would be expected of the exploitation of any valuable commodity. Cut the largest trees near the beach and streams first. Then cut the smaller ones and get those farther from the streams. Hack away at the job with never a thought of conservation or replanting. A man who lives in Miami, Florida, recently came upon a couple of truckloads of mahogany crotches on Key Largo. These had been tossed aside when the branches of the trees were cut for the ribs of the old wooden sailing vessels. Mahogany is very resistant to decay and to termites, and these crotches were in excellent condition. Crotch mahogany exhibits beautiful figure. This chapter is written by the light of a lamp made from a billet of mahogany cut from one of the ribs of a wrecked ship on the coast of Key Largo. The wreck had lain on the beach for probably fifty years, and yet a couple of plane strokes across the billet revealed bright wood. A firm in New York acquired, a few years back, some beautiful mahogany from the heavy timbers used in a building in Cuba. This building was erected, according to history, by one of the men who came over with Columbus on his second voyage.

The laurel family (the Lauraceae), in which we find sassafras, cinnamon, and camphor[4], and the myrtle family (Myrtaceae), that includes clove and eucalyptus, also contribute a great number of species of cabinet woods. In fact, the legume, mahogany, laurel, and myrtle families supply very nearly half of all the finest woods

---

[4]Earlier in the chapter we mentioned Oregon myrtle, also a member of the family Lauraceae.

in the world, and well over half of the commercially important cabinet woods.

Trees related to persimmon yield the woods known as ebony. There are many species in several parts of the world from which this black wood may be obtained. However, not all ebonies are solid black. Some, like the camogong of the Philippines, are rich brownish-black; while the coromandel of the East Indies is mottled or striped brown and black, and is used where a vigorous effect is desired. The persimmon, native to North America, does not produce ebony in commercial quantities, although a little may be formed in the heart of very old trees or around wounds on the trunk. Wood of some of the native persimmon trees, however, could pass for coromandel.

The ebonies, similar to many other fine woods, are very hard and heavy. It could not be difficult to list twenty different species of beautiful woods heavy enough to sink in water when dry. Key Largo ironwood when dry has a specific gravity of 1.4, which means that it is nearly half again as heavy as water. Of course such species are even heavier when freshly cut and full of sap. In getting them out of the jungle, it is necessary to cut two light trunks to support the one heavy one before it can be floated down a river to port. Certain of the very hard and heavy woods have special uses. Thus, snakewood (in the mulberry family), crabwood (genus *Gymnanthes* in Euphorbiaceae), and several others are used for walking sticks and, formerly, for umbrella handles. Lignum vitae from South America has long been used for bearings for the propeller shafts of oceangoing vessels.

The prices paid for some of the cabinet woods, as one would expect, are often considerable, especially where high figure, great beauty, and rarity are concerned. Highly figured logs of African mahogany (*Khaya ivorensis*) have sold for as much as twelve thousand dollars. Such a log could easily have a diameter of six feet and a length of twenty feet and would be rotary cut into veneer 1/28″ in thickness.

Single logs of oriental wood (*Cryptocarya Palmerstoni*, in the family Lauraceae, native to Queensland, Australia) sometimes yield as much as fifty thousand square feet of veneer, enough to make a ten-foot strip almost a mile in length.

In making veneers, the log is soaked in hot water until it will slice fairly easily, and then, depending on the figure of the wood, it is either rotary sliced (unrolled over the cutting blade like a great roll of paper) or sliced tangentially or radially by a straight shearing action. The way in which it will be sliced is determined by the figure of the wood. Some of the harder woods must be sawed into veneers.

Veneers have, in the past, often gained a poor reputation for themselves because they tended to crack and peel. However, well made veneers, glued with some of the splendid present-day bonding materials, have many advantages for certain uses. First, well-made veneer pieces are stronger and less apt to warp than solid wood. Second, many of the most highly figured woods would be prohibitive in cost, because of their relative scarcity, if used in the solid state. Third, only with veneer is strict matching of figure possible. To see why this is so, place your hands flat together. Now open them. If you cut through a certain part of the log, the two faces can be matched just as your right and left hand would match. Finally, many of the burl figures, because of their structure, would not be usable unless backed by straight-grained wood. They would be too apt to split or crack otherwise.

Burls, or burrs, the wart-like growths found on trees, have very characteristic, irregular grain, caused by the development of many buds or growing points. They often make extremely attractive veneers. Amboyna burl, from the East Indies, is considered to have the most beautiful figure of all. In it the small knots that characterize burl figures are surrounded by concentric circles, and these glow in a variety of colors like a summer sunset. Maidou burl, from a closely related tree, is not far behind in beauty and costliness. Of great interest historically are the *Tetraclinis* (thuja) burls from a conifer that grows in the mountains of North Africa. These were highly prized by the cultured Romans and Greeks. Cicero, two thousand years ago, is reported to have paid the equivalent of fifty thousand dollars for a banquet table ornamented with these beautiful thuja[5] burls.

Nearly all, if not all, burls are growths resulting from injuries. *Tetraclinis* burls are said to result from the native custom of burning over, for farming, the areas where the tree grows. Gathering these particular burls is a matter of grubbing them out of the ground — after you find them. The color varies from medium to very dark brown, with a leathery appearance.

---

[5]The genus *Thuja* includes our arborvitae. Although the name is applied to *Tetraclinis* burls, the two trees are in different genera, and the name is, in this case, a misnomer.

Carpathian elm burls are highly decorative. These were widely used a few years back, for example, in the interior finish of expensive custom-built automobiles. In northern Scandinavia and Finland the European white birch responds to injury from small boring larvae by producing the beautiful alpine or Karelian burls. These are lustrous, creamy white in color, with irregular dark brown lines. French designers use Karelian burl figure for cigarette cases and other luxury items. Oregon Myrtle often produces very attractive light colored burls; and olive trees, because of their gnarled manner of growth, are often practically solid burl figure. North American black ash frequently develops very attractively figured burls. They also occur frequently on our hard and soft maples and cherry trees. Burl figure is so attractive that the woods are often used in jewelry.

Ripple figure is fairly common. It is also called "fiddleback," because rippled or curly maple was commonly used for violin backs in Europe. Crotches frequently produce "plume" or "flame" figure. Aspen often produces beautiful flame figure, while mahogany crotches came into use soon after the discovery of America. Several tropical woods, having particolored markings suggestive of the plumage of birds, are called "partridge woods."

Many woods have characteristic and decorative waxlike vascular (or xylem) rays that show up prominently in "quarter-sawed" lumber, that is, cut along the radii of the trunk. Oak and beech are common examples. The pores of still other woods add much to their appearance. In trees with annual rings, that is, trees grown where there is a definite summer and winter (or wet and dry) season, these pores show up most prominently in the tangential cut (cut at right angles to the radii and tangentially to the annual rings). Many woods are prominently lined or striped. As for colors in wood, the range is all the way from white to black, with practically everything in between, even greenish.

If a wood is desired for any special purpose, the choice will usually be limited only by the pocketbook. Nature offers about anything that can be paid for. Some woods, such as northern red cedar and camphorwood, are ideal for clothes chests because of their moth-repellent ethereal oils and attractive scent.

There is a sort of romance, and also a lot of hard work, heat, and sweat connected with the harvest of many of our tropical woods, which we must pass up here for lack of space. However, when Kipling spoke of "elephints a pilin' teak," he was painting a true picture. Teak logs are heavy, and elephants are worked only three hours a day, so large herds of the pachyderms are maintained in the teak forests.

Logging in the tropics is much different from logging in the temperate regions. In the latter there are vast areas with a very few tree species — in some cases a single species. The problem of sorting and handling logs is thus relatively simple. In the tropics there may be two hundred tree species per acre. If the lumberman is cutting mahogany, for example, he may find only a few trees per acre suitable for cutting. Transportation is an important factor in tropical logging operations. In many places the start of the rainy season marks the end, for all practical purposes, of overland transport until the next dry season. There disease is much more of a problem than in the temperate zone. In some tropical countries unstable governments are an additional hazard to all such enterprises.

Scientific forestry in the tropics involves three primary considerations: first, learning what uses may be made of as many as possible of the trees on the area to be logged and learning how to handle the lumber in such a way that it will arrive on the market in condition to be used; second, creating a profitable market for the bulk of the product; and last, harvesting the timber in such a way as to insure a continuing supply of valuable lumber from the same area.

Thus we see that trees are of fundamental importance to man for holding the good earth together, for helping to maintain an equable climate, for their asthetic value, and for our great parks and woodlands. Finally, trees are sources of great wealth through all of the many products we derive from them.

ADDITIONAL READING

Many of the older publications here listed are probably out of print. Some of these, however, are still available. If it is known that the book is out of print, this in indicated. Many of these books may be found in the larger libraries.

CONSERVATION OF OUR FORESTS:

Careers in Forestry; Forest Service Miscellaneous Publication No. 249; U. S. Dept. of Agriculture, Washington, D. C. 1957 (15¢) (Obtainable from Supt. of Documents, Washington, D. C.)

Carhart, Arthur H., *Timber in Your Life;* J. H. Lippincott Co., Philadelphia, Pa., 1955. (A splendid, popular book. All should read it, especially would-be forest rangers.)

Chase, Stuart, *Rich Land Poor Land;* McGraw-Hill Cook Co., Inc., New York, 1936. (Out of print.)

Coyle, D. C., *Conservation, An American Story of Conflict and Accomplishment;* Rutgers University Press, New Brunswick, N. J., 1957.
Greeley, William B., *Forests and Men;* Doubleday and Co., Inc., Garden City, N. Y., 1951. (History of the forest conservation movement in the United States.)
Guise, Cedric H., *The Management of Farm Woodlands;* McGraw-Hill, New York, 1950.
Hawley, Ralph C., and Paul W. Stickel, *Forest Protection;* John Wiley and Sons, Inc., N. Y. City, 1948. (Wiley publishes a long series of technical books concerned with forestry practices.)
Parkins, A. E., and J. R. Whitaker, *Our Natural Resources and Their Conservation;* John Wiley and Sons, Inc., New York, 1936.
Parsons, R. L., *Conservation of American Resources;* Prentiss-Hall, Inc., Englewood Cliff, N. J., 1956.
Preston, John F., *Developing Farm Woodlands;* McGraw-Hill, N. Y. City, 1954.
Yard, Robert Sterling, *Our Federal Lands;* Charles Scribner's Sons, New York, 1928. (Out of print.)

TREE IDENTIFICATION:
Baerg, Harry, *How to Know the Western Trees,* W. C. Brown, 1955.
Brown, H. P., *Trees of Northeastern United States, Native and Naturalized;* Christopher Publishing House, Boston, Mass., 1938. (This is a fine book; good key; out of print.)
Dudley, R. H., *Our American Trees;* Thomas Y. Crowell Publishing Co., N. Y. City, 1956.
Eliot, W. A., *Forest Trees of the Pacific Coast;* G. P. Putnam's Sons, 2 West 45th St., N. Y. City, 1938. (Good photographs.)
Emerson, A. I., and C. M. Weed, *Our Trees, How to Know Them;* J. B. Lippincott Co., Philadelphia, Pa., 1959. (Good key and photographs.)
Graves, A. H., *Illustrated Guide to Trees and Shrubs;* Harper & Bros., N. Y. City, 1956.
Grimm, William C., *Familiar Trees of North America;* Harper, 1967.
Harlow, William M., *Fruit Key and Twig Key;* Dover, 1946.
Hough, Romeyn B., *Handbook of the Trees of the Northern States and Canada East of the Rocky Mountains;* The Macmillan Co., N. Y. City, 1947.
Hylander, Clarence J., *Trees and Trails;* The Macmillan Co., N. Y. City, 1952.
Leavitt, R. G., *The Forest Trees of New England;* Arnold Arboretum, Harvard University, Cambridge, Mass., 1932. (There is no key, but the illustrations are very good.)
Makins, F. K., *Identification of Trees and Shrubs;* E. P. Dutton & Co., Inc., 300 Fourth Avenue, N. Y. City, 1949. (Good text for beginners.)
Otis, C. H., *Michigan Trees;* University of Michigan Press, Ann Arbor,

Michigan, 1931. (This is well illustrated, simple, and has a good key.)

Preston, R. J., *Rocky Mountain Trees;* Iowa State College Press, Ames, Iowa, 1947. (Valuable for trees in this region.)

Rehder, Alfred, *Manual of Cultivated Trees and Shrubs Hardy in North America;* The Macmillan Co., New York City, 1940. (Very thorough and complete. A little complex for the beginner.)

Sargent, C. S., *Manual of the Trees of North America;* Houghton Mifflin Co., N. Y. City, 1933; Revised 1962. (Standard text for the continent; all trees well illustrated. Good key.)

Tresidder, M. C., *Trees of Yosemite;* Stanford University Press, Stanford University, California, 1948. (Good key.)

Zim, Herbert S., and Alexander C. Martin, *Trees;* Simon and Schuster, N. Y. City, 1956. (One of the *Golden Guides,* published in full color. The paper-bound edition is sold at $1.00. A bargain for the beginner.)

FINE WOODS AND LUMBER:

A Handbook of Empire Timbers; Dept. of Scientific and Industrial Research, Forest Products Research Lab. (England, His Majesty's Stationary Office, London, 1939.) (Probably no longer in print.)

Baker, R. T., *The Hardwoods of Australia;* The Government of New South Wales, Sydney, Australia, 1919. (A beautiful book; much of it in color. May still be available.)

Constantine, Albert, *Know Your Woods;* Constantine, 1959.

Gill, Tom, *Tropical Forests of the Caribbean;* Pan American, Washington, D. C., 1931.

Howard, Alexander L., *Timbers of the World;* Macmillan & Co., New York, 1948.

Latham, Bryan, *Wood from Forest to Man;* Verry, 1964.

Record, Samuel J., and Robert W. Hess, *Timbers of the New World;* Yale University Press, New Haven, Conn., 1944. (This is the standard text on all woods of the Americas.)

Reyes, Luis J., *Philippine Woods;* T. B. #7, Bureau of Forestry, Manila, 1938. (Probably now out of print; available through larger technical libraries.)

Sherwood, Malcolm H., *From Forest to Furniture;* W. W. Norton and Co., New York, 1936.

Swain, E. H. F., *Timbers and Forest Products of Queensland;* Queensland Forestry Service, Govt. Printer, Brisbane, Australia, 1928. (Still available a few years back.)

CHAPTER 21

A Career or a Hobby in the World of Plants

ANY people have a deep, natural interest in plants. This interest may become evident at a very early age. My earliest memory recalls a walk with my father in a woods near our home in Tacoma, Washington. We came upon a long-abandoned homesite. Although the buildings had all but rotted to oblivion, there were still many clumps of bellis daisies flourishing bravely. I insisted that we go back home for a spade to transplant some of them to our own flower border. When I was not much over five years old I solemnly told my father that the pansy and violet were related. "I think you are right," he replied. This early interest, largely self-directed, has never left me.

The fact that you have read this far in the book would indicate that you also are interested in plants. If you want a hobby, or even a career, in the world of plants, the choice is very wide. One purpose of this book has been to give the reader some idea of how wide that choice can be.

In research and teaching fields, there are positions in the U. S. Department of Agriculture, in the Agricultural Extension Service, in high schools, and in the many academic and agricultural colleges. Many private enterprises hire men trained in botanical fields. These include canners, seed producers, nurseries, and many other industries based on the myriad uses of plant products. Most of the better positions require at least a college degree, and many of them necessitate training beyond four years of college. The Department of Agriculture's Handbook No. 45, entitled "Career Service Opportunities in the United States Department of Agriculture," outlines qualification requirements, nature of work, responsibilities, and opportunities for many positions. In relation to work with plants, this handbook lists several possible fields that, with the Department of Agriculture, would be concerned largely with research, but that, in colleges, could be either research or teaching or both. Careers in botanical lines include:

Botany — General study of plants, fundamental to all scientific plant work. Usually the person interested in plants, after he has achieved a good command of general botany, goes on to one or more of the following fields:

Agronomy — Study of crops in relation to soil, cultural methods, and water supply. The field is so vast and the problems so numerous that many who enter this field narrow their interests principally to a single crop. There will be opportunities in agronomy as long as man depends on crops for food and other uses.

Systematics and Taxonomy — Study of plant relationships and plant identification, basic to all other branches. In this area there are as many sub-areas as there are special groups, for example:

Agrostology — Study of grasses
Dendrology — Study of trees
Phycology — Study of algae
Bryology — Study of mosses

And there are many others, with divisions within each field. For example, one man might become an expert on tropical marine algae, another on North American fresh-water algae, etc. Remember that complete floras (catalogs of species and their relationships) are still lacking for many plant groups in many parts of the world.

The following special fields include studies other than purely systematic work with the group concerned:

Plant Exploration and Introduction — Searching the world for valuable plant materials.

Mycology — Study of fungi. The work here could range all the way from production of antibiotics to the relation of pathogenic fungi to diseases of plants and animals. The production of new antibiotics alone, as we indicated elsewhere in the book, is a field that will remain wide open for years. There are doubtless many antibiotics as good as, or better than, penicillin, waiting to be discovered.

Phytopathology — Studies on the many diseases of plants and their control. We have shown in Chapter 16 that the livelihood of whole groups of people may be wiped out by plant diseases. Crop failures due to plant diseases have even resulted in the starvation of millions.

Microbiology — The study of organisms, including plants, so small that they must be observed by use of the microscope and by other special techniques. There are a great many possibilities here. The expert might, for example, specialize in the study of the microscopic plants that make up the food supply of the somewhat larger organisms upon which some of our commercial fish depend. On the other hand, he might specialize in the fungi that inhabit the soil and their relations to other organisms and to their physical and chemical surroundings.

Bacteriology — Research with the microscopic plants we call bacteria, some of which are beneficial, others pathogenic to plants or animals. We usually think of the bacteriologist as working only with organisms harmful to man, but this is simply one of many fields in bacteriology. There are careers open, for example, in such special studies as bacteria in relation to sewage disposal, or the use of bacteria to produce certain chemicals in commercial quantities.

Botanical Entomology — Covering the subject of insects in connection with plants. This would involve methods of control of insects that attack our plants, as well as studies of insects beneficial to plants. See Chapter 17 for more on this. The botanical entomologist would be well grounded in both botany and entomology and, in addition, would become a specialist in whatever segment of this vast area he chose to enter.

Plant Physiology — The study of the manner in which plants carry on their vital processes. This would include, among other things, the special field of plant nutrition. Just to mention a few of the other fields, there have been many valuable studies in the recent past of day length in relation to flowering. This is vital to a florist who wishes to have all of his chrysanthemums in full bloom by a certain date, or his poinsettias at their peak at Christmas time. By proper use of lights and curtains for shade, this can be done very exactly. The plant physiologist may meet such problems as the determination of the exact conditions required to insure the maximum production of different plant products, for example, latex, tannin, fibre, or drugs.

Ecology — The study of the relation of plants to their environment and to each other. There are as many avenues open here as there are environments on earth and in the water, with side paths leading off each avenue.

Morphology — Study of plant structures. This field is as wide as the plant kingdom, and so much remains to be done. For example, in the course of studies in which I was once engaged on a disease of corn, I discovered that there were a series of shoots within the leaf sheaths below the corn ear, harking back, doubtless, to some ancestor in which each one of these developed and produced seed. I found further that a high percentage of these were infected with the pathogenic organism I was studying (*Nigrospora oryzae*). I was astonished to find that, although corn has been studied intensively for years, these obvious structures had never been named. Because they are never dveloped into ears, and because of their position in the axils of the leaves, I named them "arrested axillary shoots." With man so fundamentally dependent on plants, it becomes obvious that the better we understand them, the better we can employ them for our needs. This applies not only to commercially important plants, for who can tell what plant may become commercially important tomorrow?

Cytology — Study of the cell as an entity. Because the cell is the fundamental work unit in all plants (and animals), the importance of understanding all we can about the cell and its processes is obvious. We are beginning to understand how cells multiply, how they prepare for sexual reproduction, and the like. There are important studies in progress at present on the desoxyribosenucleic acid materials that make up the genes, those wonderful structures that determine plant (and animal) characteristics. These studies seem to be bringing us closer to the point where man can create living organisms. There is other research in progress on the changing of genes, and through such changes on the characteristics of plants by chemicals such as colchicine, by X-rays, and by other means; and several valuable contributions to our cultivated plants have already resulted.

Plant Anatomy and Histology — Study of the cells and plant tissues as revealed under the microscope. Such studies would extend cytological studies to the functioning of cells in larger group units.

Plant Genetics — An examination of the manner in which plants inherit parental characteristics. Plant breeding is applied plant genetics. All of our new crop varieties are the result of studies in theoretical and applied genetics. This field is boundless, fascinating, and commercially very important.

Paleobotany — Study of ancient plants. There are many specialized fields of study in this area. See Chapter 13. The vastness of this field of study leaves room for many capable students.

Pollen Analysis and Related Material — See Chapters 6 and 12. Research here could be in fields as far apart as studies connected with pollen allergies to those connected with paleobotany or even archeology, since, through fossil pollen, we can reconstruct in part the flora of any given point in time and place.

Medical Botany — See Chapter 12. In spite of the advent of synthetic drugs, many important advances are still being made in the medicinal use of plant products.

Weed and Brush Control — See Chapter 18. The losses occasioned by weeds and other undesirable plants make it necessary to maintain an army of research and operational workers in these fields in all civilized countries.

Plant Toxicology — See Chapter 11. Studies here may be as diverse as control of toxic plants on cattle and sheep ranges, relation of toxic plant substances to possible medical uses, or to plant defense mechanisms depending on toxic chemicals.

Forestry — Scientific management of resources. See Chapter 20. Silviculture is one of the studies in this area. Since there are a great many uses for trees, there are obviously many fields of specialization possible here.

Wood Anatomy — and other studies related to wood, its identification, characteristics, and uses. See Chapter 20.

Conservation is such an important field that it deserves special consideration. Conservation workers are trained in agronomy, forestry, fire control methods, range biology, engineering, soils, farm management, and public relations. The reader will find brief discussions of conservation in Chapters 18 and 20.

Conservation of our forests, grasslands, great scenic areas, and plant sanctuaries is of vital importance to everyone. A critical look at the many parts of the world, including parts of the United States, where, through lack of proper conservation methods, forests, grazing areas, and farm lands have been allowed to slip into ruin, would be sufficient to convince any intelligent person of this fact. Some authorities say that, in the absence of conservation practices, the United States could lose practically all of its forests, range land, and good farmland in as little as one hundred years.

There are many interesting careers for the able and devoted in the several fields of conservation of our plant and soil resources. Much research is in progress at the present time, and there will continue to be positions for trained men. There are careers open in range and forest management, in the proper management of our crop lands, and in public relations.

Beyond teaching, research, and public service opportunities, there are the many other possibilities in horticulture and agronomy, including such obvious examples as the several branches of field and truck farming, nursery work, orchard work, seed growing, greenhouse management, and floriculture. Closely related are land-scape architecture, tree surgery, greens-keeping, and a host of other special fields. Well-trained, intelligent, and energetic entrepreneurs in any of these pursuits carve out interesting and profitable careers.

Hobbies for all ages are abundant in the world of plants. For the studious amateur, many of the career suggestions will be of interest. There are so many possibilities for all ages in the botanical part of nature study — flowers, trees, grasses, their collection and preservation — that the choice is almost unlimited. Gardening, with all its special interests, has been a hobby for centuries.

Organizations interested in helping with such hobbies are plenti-ful, too. For the younger enthusiasts, there are such groups as the Bluebirds (7-9 years), leading to the Camp Fire Girls (10-14), and the parallel Brownies and Girl Scouts, the Cub Scouts and Boy Scouts for boys, and dozens of others. It is interesting to note that the Camp Fire Girls have, as a part of their official wish, "to know about trees and flowers and birds." The Girl Scouts include in their program a well-organized project of Ranger Aides, devoted to furthering conservation practices. I am informed by Miriam R. Ephraim of the National Jewish Welfare Board that all their camps conduct extensive nature programs. It is general practice with almost all of the many private and public camps over the nation to provide instruction in nature study, with much of the emphasis on plants and conservation practices. Many of our national history museums cater, as far as possible, to botanical interests among young people. The American Museum of Natural History, for example, publishes a series of mimeographed sheets covering nature study hobbies. The Brooklyn Botanic Garden offers quite a series of courses related to plants and has been a pioneer in this respect. Among many other offerings, it features a garden for the blind and classes in the Bonsai method of dwarfing plants, a Japanese art. The New York Botanical Garden has more recently established such programs. Their 1957-1958 brochure lists such courses as Plant Identification, House Plants, Flower Arrangement, How to Propagate Shrubs and Trees, Plant Workshop, Outdoor Gardencraft, Indoor Gardencraft, Flower and Vegetable Gardening, Planning the Home Grounds, Plant Breeding, Field Botany, How to Propagate Garden and Greenhouse Plants, and many others.[1]

---

[1]Both the Brooklyn Botanic Garden and the New York Botanical Gar-dens are membership societies, with members residing in most of the States.

Arnold Arboretum, Barnes Arboretum, Hatheway School of Conservation Education in South Lincoln, Massachusetts, and several other institutions offer many similar courses.

The National Audubon Society maintains summer camps in Maine, Connecticut, Wisconsin, and California for training teachers, youth leaders, and others in nature study and conservation. About half the time is spent on plant study. The Audubon Society also sponsors the Audubon Junior Clubs, the leaders of which are supplied with study materials and instructions. The Audubon Junior Clubs cooperate as closely as possible with other youth organizations.

Many of our colleges and universities offer courses of interest to students of nature, horticulture, or conservation. Obviously our many agricultural colleges and schools of forestry are in such work up to their ears. Some of our larger public schools have gardening projects. The real pioneers in this field are probably the Cleveland Public Schools that started a student garden program in 1915. This is still very active. Mr. Paul Young directed this program for over twenty-five years and has done a splendid job.

Future Farmers of America and the 4-H organization, with members drawn largely from rural groups, stress the phases of agiculture and horticulture that are directly related to crop production, with a healthy emphasis on conservation practices.

For adults there are almost as many garden clubs in the country as there are towns with populations over five thousand. Such an amount of activity and interest is a fair gauge of the importance of plants and gardening to our way of life. William H. Hull, director of the Men's Garden Clubs of America, wrote, "Man, crowded increasingly into suburban standards of living ..., is involuntarily being turned toward spectator sports as an outlet for the sports need. However, this does not provide him with the physical exercise necessary to sound mental and physical well being. . . . Gardening meets all these needs for men. When done with skill, it requires a standard beyond that of shooting an eighty in golf; it becomes a real art and a challenge toward constant improvement. It can become a door toward plant improvement and plant breeding. It supplies the opportunity to be out of doors; it gives one the further pleasure of beautifying one's own premises; and perhaps most of all, it serves man's basic need of being creative."

The reader may wish to become affiliated with one or both of them and participate in their programs.

Mr. Hull lists a membership of over eighteen thousand with 190 affiliated clubs in the Men's Garden Clubs of America group alone. There are half a million members of the National Council of State Garden Clubs which, in some localities, include men.

In addition to the many garden clubs in all parts of the country, there are many local, state, national, and international societies, both commercial and amateur, devoted to the culture and improvement of certain plants or groups of plants. The enthusiast whose interest centers on any one subject will be well advised to become affiliated with one or more of the societies devoted to the plant of his choice. Such memberships permit exchange of information on culture of the plant concerned, exchange of plant material, access to exhibits, and a community of interests. Some of these societies have permanent headquarters. Others move about with change of officers. However, the current address of any one society may usually be obtained through the library of the United States Department of Agriculture.

There are societies devoted to African violets, begonias, bulbs, cacti and succulents, camellias, carnations, chrysanthemums, dahlias, delphiniums, epiphyllums, ferns, fuchsias, gladioli, gourds, hemerocallis, hibiscus, holly, iris, orchids, penstemons, peonies, poppies, primroses, rhododendrons, rock gardens, roses, shade trees, snapdragons, tulips, and wild flowers. There are still other societies concerned with the culture, usually commercial, of practically every crop, even including societies for the cultivation of mangoes and the several nut crops.

A detailed catalog of the hobby possibilities in the world of plants would be very long. Here are a few suggestions:

1. Growing something, with choices that may range from bulbs or potted plants or window boxes for city dwellers or invalids to rock gardens, vegetable, flower, or small-fruit culture and even orchards or arboretums.

2. Nature study, including identification of wild flowers, shrubs, ferns, trees, aquatic plants, fungi, lichens, or the relation of plants to their environments and to each other.

3. General botanical studies, such as general botany, systematic botany (plant relationships), mycology (fungi), dendrology (trees), plant genetics, plant pathology, plant physiology, and many more. These will be of particular interest to the more studious and experimentally minded enthusiast, but it is astonishing how rapidly a rank amateur can begin to find his way around in any of them.

4. Experimentation and techniques, for example, in cultural methods, plant propagation, soil fertility, and soil analysis, or the preparing of sections for examination under the microscope (an involved science).

5. Collections, for example, dried herbarium specimens, fungi and spore prints, woods, twigs, seeds, and so on. Get some professional help on this if possible.

6. Landscaping, which may be rather simple for a small lot, or very ambitious indeed. There are many books available on this.

7. Flower arrangement, with many techniques available, both Occidental and Oriental. This may vary from arrangements for the home or church to such ambitious projects as flower shows.

8. Plant photography offers many interesting possibilities and, if you become rather expert, it can be a good source of income.

Let no one feel that a love of plants is a trivial or unworthy thing. Great people of all ages and in all lands have loved plants. Many contributions to botany have been made by people who were not professional botanists. One example may be cited to illustrate.

I have recently read *A Botanist in Southern Africa* by John Hutchinson. It is interesting to note that the foreword of the book was written by the great soldier-stateman, Field Marshal Jan Christian Smuts, who also organized several of Hutchinson's expeditions and accompanied him as a rather well-trained botanist. I quote from his foreword:

> I have always been a lover of plants. As a farmer's son in the old Cape Colony days I grew up close to nature and all her intimate ways; and when later I studied botany at college I used to accompany Professor Marloth, a great figure in South African botany, on his botanical expeditions. Botany was a natural hobby to me, and my holidays were usually spent in long rambles over the veld and on the mountains of what was, and still remains, one of the floral paradises of the world. The bond with nature and plants was not so much scientific as personal, and deepened into a spiritual influence of an abiding character. Thus in the busy, crowded years of later life I took my relaxation and spent my occasional holidays in botanical rambles, away from the human pressure which is of all the most exciting and oppressive. For to the busy mind there is no release, no easing off comparable with that of just wandering away and tramping over the veld, absorbed in the wild life of plant and beast. It is the truly wholesome escape from life's oppressive exigence.

An extremely important and rapidly expanding field for work with plants is that of occupational therapy in its many ramifications. Mrs. Arthur Richie has expressed it thus: "... horticulture *is* a therapy. ...." Man's roots in the soil are deep, and many a harried citizen finds peace of mind through working with or association with plants.

Work with plants can be adapted, in one form or another, to very nearly all therapeutic needs — for shut-ins and patients largely disabled, for convalescents, for the partially disabled, or for the physically fit. There are so many diverse plant interests that it is not difficult to find one within the interests and abilities of anyone. Experts in this work stress the importance of allowing the patient to select his field of activity with regard to his interests and abilities. It is also obviously important that the work be carried on with the full approval and cooperation of attending physicians and institutions concerned.

Here are a few of the many possibilities beyond growing something:

1. Flower arrangements, using either fresh or dried materials.

2. There are available many moving pictures, quite a number of them in color, related to plant life, horticulture, conservation, plant exploration, and botanical research.

3. For the blind, emphasis is often placed on herb gardens. The fragrance of the plants employed is a valuable compensation for the lack of sight.

4. One group, according to Miss Virginia Sculling, physical therapist with the New York Department of Mental Hygiene, grew their own basket willows, cut and stripped the willow withes, and wove them into baskets. Another group grew flax, processed it into fibres, made thread of the fibre, then wove the thread into linen cloth.

5. Ambulatory patients may even undertake rather ambitious projects, for example, a flower show. A group in the Veteran's Hospital, Northport, Long Island, has held an annual flower show at the hospital each year since 1946. There were over a thousand exhibits entered in a recent show, with nearly five thousand people in attendance. These shows have had excellent write-ups in several newspapers, including the *New York Times*.

6. Patients nearly ready to return to society may be taught some horticultural or related profession. Mr. N. J. Pierce of the Veteran's Administration Hospital, Northport, Long Island, writes, "Long

Island has many beautiful estates and numerous commercial growers. Many of our patients, upon discharge from the hospital, are able to qualify for employment, and in this way earn a livelihood."

Therapy can be interpreted in a narrow sense, as applying to those commonly considered physically or mentally ill. In a wide sense, therapy includes all techniques that may be employed to keep all mankind in the best possible mental and physical health. Thus, we should consider many of the inmates of penitentiaries as people who are socially ill. I had some experience with the establishment of a penitentiary school. I observed that, to students in this school, science meant one thing only, scientific farming. For children born and reared in the concrete jungles of our big cities, the opportunity to participate in a garden project, or to hike in the woods, or to camp, must certainly be considered a special form of therapy.

There is still another increasingly important problem that finds a part of its answer in work with plants. Modern medical science and sanitation have greatly lengthened the average life span of civilized man. As with all great changes for the better, this increase in life span has created many new problems. The proportion of older people has greatly increased. There is now a greater opportunity, or often a pressure, for early retirement from business activities. The years following retirement could and should be the fruition years — potentially a happy period. Too often the disruption of long-established habits, the feeling of being no longer necessary and not really wanted, the feeling of being in the way, turns this time into bitter, lonely, boring old age. An unhappy older person is, in a very real sense, an invalid. In fact, it has been shown that retired men with no hobbies have an average life expectancy of eighteen months.

What are older people to do with themselves? Most of them start this period in full command of their mental powers and most of their physical powers. The science of geriatrics has already grown up to face this problem. While there are many avenues of approach, it is obvious that the world of plants offers a wealth of material useful in geriatrics. The several possibilities listed in the discussion of occupational therapy can be applied, with suitable modifications, to this need.

With this we close a chapter that could easily be expanded into many volumes.

Index of Principal Subjects